Malaysian Trees in Colour

Malaysian Trees in Colour

CHIN HOONG FONG
M. AGR. SC., PH. D. (MELB.), F.I. BIOL.

PROFESSOR
AGRONOMY AND HORTICULTURE DEPARTMENT
UNIVERSITI PERTANIAN MALAYSIA

IVAN. C. ENOCH
B. SC. (HONS.) (WALES)

TROPICAL PRESS SDN. BHD.
56–2 JALAN MAAROF
59100 KUALA LUMPUR
MALAYSIA

TROPICAL PRESS SDN. BHD.
56–2 JALAN MAAROF
59100 KUALA LUMPUR
MALAYSIA

First published 1988
Reprinted 1991
Reprinted 1995

Perpustakaan Negara Malaysia   Cataloguing in Publication Data

Chin, Hoong Fong
  Malaysian Trees in Colour/ Chin Hoong Fong,
  Ivan C. Enoch.

1. Trees—Malaysia. I. Enoch, Ivan C.
II. Title.
634.909595

ISBN 967-73-0009-1

PRINTED BY
ART PRINTING WORKS SDN. BHD.
29, JALAN RIONG, 59100 KUALA LUMPUR
MALAYSIA

We are like trees:
We must create new leaves,
new directions,
in order to grow.

Contents

Preface	xvii
In Memory of Trees	xix
Introduction	1
Trees	15
Fruit Trees	105
Forest and Plantation Trees	127
Palms and Bamboos	143
Propagation, Planting and Maintenance	165
Index	172
Appendix-List of Trees without Illustrations	176

Many a tree is found in the wood
And every tree for its use is good
Some for the strength of the gnarled root
Some for the sweetness of flower or fruit

~Henry van Dyke

Photo Contest '82

Theme: TREES
... aesthetically beautiful, majestic, functional and vital for life — OUR LIFE

FIRST PRIZE

A Place for Worship

If the roots are deep, no fear that the wind will uproot the tree — Anon

Stamps

Lemon Tree

When I was just a lad of ten, my father said to me
Come here and take a lesson from the lovely lemon tree
"Don't put your faith in love my boy" my father said to me
I fear you'll find that love is like the lovely lemon tree

Chorus:

Lemon tree very pretty, and the lemon flower is sweet
But the fruit of the poor lemon is impossible to eat
Lemon tree very pretty and the lemon flower is sweet
But the fruit of the poor lemon is impossible to eat

One day beneath the lemon tree, my love and I did lie
A girl so sweet that when she smiled the stars rose in the sky
We passed that summer lost in love beneath that lemon tree
The music of her laughter hid my father's words from me

One day she left without a word, she took away the sun
And in the dark she left behind I knew what she had done
She left me for another, it's a common tale but true
A sadder man, but wiser now, I sing this song to you

Preface

Malaysian Trees in Colour is the third of a series of books on the rich flora and fauna of Malaysia. This country is well-known for the thousands of plant species such as timber, fruits plantation crops and ornamentals. Because of the luxuriant plant growth and tropical climate this country is evergreen all the year round; a few species of deciduous trees turn brown and shed their leaves.

Undisturbed, the natural beauty on earth is almost perfect. However, in this modern world, men have cut down forest trees, plant food crops, live in cities and built highways and skyscrapers, irrevocably upsetting the natural environment. The world we live in has become artificial, due to the change in the natural landscape. It is hard to believe that all the changes made by man are wise or beneficial.

Professional town planners and landscape designers must be made responsible for directing society's use of land. Only recently Kuala Lumpur the Federal Capital has launched a beautification programme costing 2.5 million ringgit and other capital cities are following suit. In future, it is hoped that landscaping and gardening will be a compulsory feature in all new developments including housing.

By writing this book we aim to heighten people's awareness of the beauty of trees and the different uses of them. This book depicts over 100 species of trees, palms and bamboos which are illustrated with colour plates. It is hoped that this book will be useful to landscape architects, town planners, horticulture and landscape students, home gardeners, nurserymen, and for the interest of tourists. Brief descriptions of shrubs and trees are given on a wide range of species including flowering trees, fruit trees, plantation trees, palms and bamboos. For each species the local name, common name, botanical name and family are given and illustrated with colour plates for easy identification. Botanical names are updated, hence a few names given here may differ from an earlier book, *Malaysian Flowers in Colour* published ten years ago.

The authors would like to thank the Vice-Chancellor of Universiti Pertanian Malaysia, Professor Nayan bin Ariffin for permission to publish this book.

Universiti Pertanian Malaysia
H.F. Chin
I.C. Enoch

June 1987

In Memory of Trees

Man's existence on earth largely depends on trees. One is amazed what the trees can provide us. Everything we eat comes almost directly or indirectly from the plant kingdom. They provide us shelter, food, medicine and purify the air we breathe. In short our life depends on plants.

Plants of any shapes or sizes from the most simple to the complex are usually important to us, yet we seldom have a second thought of the trees around us except when we are looking for shade at noon or when we want to landscape our gardens.

Fortunately, among us there are some nature lovers and conservationists who will go all out to protect nature by preventing the destruction of natural forests, establishing gardens, arboretums and gene banks so that the future generation can survive and enjoy what we have at present. This may well disappear if man continues to destroy the forest indiscriminately.

To commemorate trees, songs and poems have been written about them, stamps depicting trees are produced and released by the postal departments, trees first brought into the country have commemorative plaques, such as the first rubber tree grown in Kuala Kangsar, Malaysia. It is also customary to commemorate the visits of royal dignitaries by a tree planting ceremony, thus indirectly the trees are also remembered.

Introduction

Large areas of natural forests are being destroyed every year and many species of plants will disappear because they are of no commercial value. Many of these species should be cultivated for their ornamental value, which can then be assessed and, by selection and hybridization their range can be increased. Planting of trees in all possible situations in both urban and rural areas should be encouraged strongly to provide partial compensation for the denudation of the natural forest.

Trees may be used for screening buildings. Even very tall buildings can be partly hidden (Photo I$_1$) or the planting can be so arranged that the

Photo I$_1$

buildings are viewed through the foliage (Photo I_1). Sometimes, trees are planted in courtyards, situated within a building. Such areas must have plenty of sunlight, otherwise trees cannot thrive and other plants instead have to be grown. A courtyard that is well planted with trees and shrubs makes a very welcome sight within the confines of large buildings and is most refreshing to look at. The plants also help to cut down the amount of reflected heat and glare from the outside (Photos I_2 I_3).

It is possible to plant trees very close to a building provided they do not have a root system which can block the drainage systems. Trees with dense foliage should not be planted near walls with many windows as they would make the rooms gloomy. But trees with light crowns can be used to advantage as they will not darken the rooms and will reduce considerably the amount of reflected heat. Trees with dense crowns can be planted near walls of buildings that have no windows. Many modern buildings are fully air-conditioned and by shielding the walls and windows with trees the amount of reflected heat reaching the building will be much reduced thereby increasing the efficiency of the air-conditioners. However, pruning is necessary for those trees near walls and windows (Photo I_4).

Some buildings are closed on three sides and opened on one. Trees can be grown very effectively in such places. They serve to soften the outline of the building and at the same time cutting down the heat and glare from the rooms (Photo I_5).

Fairly narrow spaces between very tall buildings can be planted effectively although the choice of

Photo I_2

Photo I_3

Photo I₄

plants is more limited (Photo I₅). Such areas receive a certain amount of sunlight but for a large part of each day they are shaded. Some palms are especially suited for planting in such areas.

In towns and cities where trees are planted on road dividers and at

Photo I₅

roundabouts they should not impede the vision of motorists. The crowns of such trees should not be less than three metres from ground level. For such areas only species which will tolerate a wide range of growing conditions can be used as they must contend with traffic fumes and more than the normal amount of reflected heat from road surfaces and walls of buildings. Also, the extent of soil surface through which rain water can penetrate to the roots may be severely restricted and this can be a cause of stress to the trees during long periods of dry weather. This is true of trees planted in car parks where the available planting space is severely restricted (Photo I₆).

Some species of trees have large heavy fruits and are unsuitable for planting in car parks, along roadsides or near paths and areas frequented by people.

Photo I₆

Such trees can be used in some parts of public parks, and in golf courses or they can be used in large planting schemes provided they are not planted near areas which are much frequented.

There is a wide variety of trees which can be used for any kind of planting scheme. More of the native species should be brought into cultivation to assess their merits as ornamentals. These species have been sorely neglected merely because they are looked upon as 'wild plants'. But many of them make well-shaped trees, tolerant of a range of growing conditions and, under controlled cultivation, selection of the better forms could be done.

Tree form and size are in great variety and so there is ample scope for selecting species to be used in different situations or for different purposes. Small trees will grow to five or six metres high, but many of the forest species can reach 40 to 60 metres. Such great height is only attained after many years of growth, and under cultivation this may not occur. When selecting the kind of trees for planting, great care must be taken to suit the physical environment because a quick-growing, large tree in a small area will become a liability.

Some trees drop their leaves periodically. These species are described as deciduous. In tropical climate, the leaf-fall usually occurs after a period of dry weather; but in temperate climate it occurs before winter. The deciduous habit or 'wintering' is useful as it provides a complete change of aspect in the landscape during the year. The only disadvantage is that once or sometimes twice a year there will be a large number of dead leaves to be swept away.

With deciduous trees the leaves from the whole crown may drop almost at the same time. But before this happens the leaves may show a dramatic change of colour as happens with rubber trees where the colour change to yellow and reddish brown before leaf-fall. In the Ketapang, the leaves become a rich red colour before they drop. The colour change might be caused by an extended dry spell. In some deciduous species leaves from one or a few branches only will drop, to give the tree an untidy or ragged appearance. After leaf-fall the new foliage may develop immediately or there may be an interval of one to four weeks before the new growth begins. Some trees produce their flowers while the branches are bare and this is well seen in rubber, mahogany, dedap, jacaranda and gliricida. If the flowers are large and plentiful the trees look very decorative. The young leaves, when they appear may be pale green or reddish in colour. Young pale green leaves give the tree a light and airy appearance until the colour darkens as they mature. Many tropical trees produce coloured young leaves and these may be white, pink, violet or bright red. This makes the tree very conspicuous and from a distance it will seem as though it is flowering. In many species with coloured young leaves, the new twigs and leaves appear very rapidly and are soft and limp, so that they hang like large coloured tassels from the tips of branches. As this new growth matures, both the leaves and the twigs gradually assume their normal positions and the colour of the leaves changes to green. This may last for about two weeks and provides a change of aspect in the way a leaf-fall or production of flowers do.

Evergreen trees hold their leaves

throughout the year and only drop the older leaves a few at a time. The branches are never bare and flushes of young leaves are produced at intervals throughout the year. Young leaves may be brightly coloured and provide a sharp contrast with the older foliage. This is well seen in the Ceylon Ironwood which has dark-green matured leaves and bright-red young leaves.

Tree crowns show wide differences in shape and size and this may be the first characteristic to consider in large-scale or restricted planting. Tree crowns may be very dense so that it is impossible to see through them or they may be very open with the branch system clearly visible and the sky easily seen through the foliage. Trees with dense crowns which remain close to the ground will prevent the growth of grass underneath until the trunks become tall and the older branches dropped away.

A tree crown may be conical, round, oval, columnar, tiered, hemispherical or flat topped (Figure 1). There are, of course, many intermediate shapes and in many species the shape of the crown will change as the trees become older. Durian, Casuarina, and Ceylon Ironwood are conical in shape when

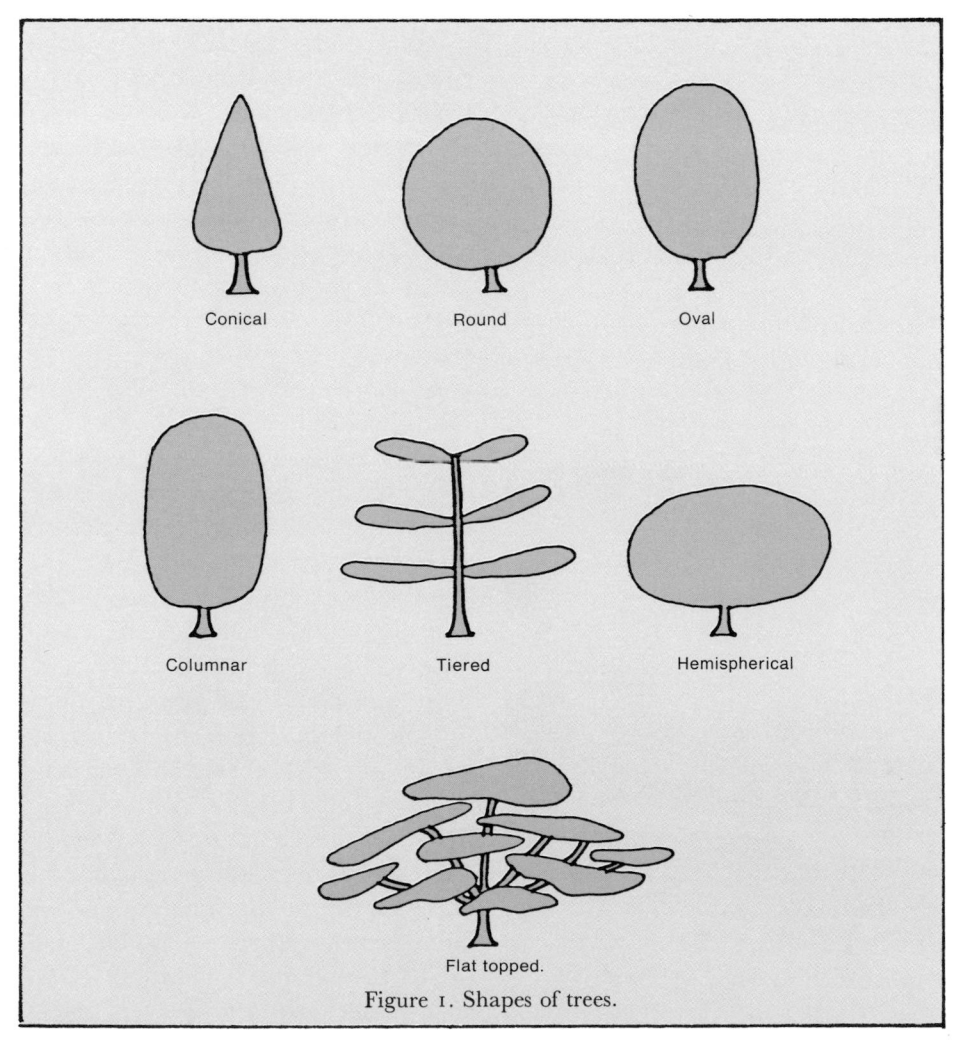

Conical   Round   Oval

Columnar   Tiered   Hemispherical

Flat topped.

Figure 1. Shapes of trees.

young but become irregular later because of the development of several main branches. This change of shape occurs slowly and the length of time involved varies with individual trees.

Some trees will tolerate pruning and can be kept to a definite shape and size as with the Casuarina and Podocarpus.

BRANCHES

The architecture of trees is influenced by the size, number and arrangement of the branches, but the general appearance of any tree will be strongly influenced by the size, form and arrangement of the leaves. The general shape of a tree crown will be largely decided by the behaviour of the leading shoot. If this continues to grow strongly throughout the life of the tree and is never overtopped by the other branches, then the tree will have a conical shape—as in many conifers. In other trees the growth of the leading shoot is much slower and the branches develop strongly so that the crown of the tree becomes broader and eventually shows a rounded

Photo I$_7$

outline. In such trees, the leading shoot may lose its dominance completely. The appearance of the whole crown is affected by the manner in which the later small twigs develop. They may be long or short and may be held almost vertically, horizontally or in a drooping manner and this will give a definite character to the tree crown. In addition, the size and form of the leaves, the manner in which they are held and distributed on the twigs will affect the whole appearance of the tree.

Most trees used for ornamental purposes will shape themselves to some extent and many will hold their lower branches for a long time while they are young. If the foliage is dense it will prevent grass and weeds from growing near the trunk of the young trees and the appearance of such trees will be neat. Often the lower branches are removed when the young plants are about two metres high so that the surrounding grass may be cut easily and also because many people feel that a clean, straight tree trunk should be developed as early as possible. In some tree species the initial growth in thickness of the trunk is slow and if the lower branches are removed, the upper ones will put out more leaves and twigs, thus making a small heavy crown. And unless the young trees are tied to a strong stake they will fall over or the trunk will snap in high winds and heavy rain. The practice of removing the lower branches early makes the tree more formal in appearance. If all the species are treated in this way, the view of the landscape can be monotonous. This appearance will persist for several years until the different species have grown sufficiently to develop their individual characteristics. Groups of trees in the centre of parks or other public areas where people move about may be treated in this way. But around the perimeter of these areas a mixture of trees and shrubs giving foliage low to the ground should be grown. This will give one the illusion of being in a rural area (Photo I$_7$). Trees planted in this way act like a screen to reduce traffic noise and fumes.

When planning a planting scheme, selection of species should be carefully made so that there is a mixture of leaf size and colour to render a group of trees a more interesting view. However, what trees to grow will depend on the size of the planting scheme and the desired effect (Photo I$_8$). Groups of two to seven trees of one species alone will appear more formal (Photo I$_9$) than a group in which several different species are used. Trees planted singly should be given plenty of space so that they can develop their characteristic crown shape which will then show to great advantage. In very large-scale planting, the skyline effect is important, and for this purpose large

Photo I$_8$

trees with crowns of distinctive shape should be used to be clearly distinguished from a distance. Planting in rows may give a plantation or 'orchard' appearance because before the crowns of the trees mingle with one another the effect will be highly artificial.

To make buildings or other land forms look natural, carefully chosen species can be so positioned that they complement the buildings or the surroundings. Such plants are viewed at relatively close range. Therefore the leaf forms and colours are more

Photo I$_9$

7

important for creating an impact on the viewer. A brief look at leaves in the next section would be useful therefore in helping to select the kinds of trees for various purposes.

LEAVES

Leaves show considerable variation in size, ranging from tiny needle like forms to very large structures one metre or more in length and width and this naturally can influence the appearance of a tree crown very strongly. Some leaves have a single blade with one or more main veins and secondary veins and there may or may not be a stalk of varying lengths. These are described as simple and are seen in mango and durian. Other leaves have two or more leaflets each with or without a short stalk and are attached to a common stalk (rachis). Each leaflet has exactly the same structure as a simple leaf. The margin of the leaf or leaflet blade may be smooth, or it may be toothed in various ways, or it may be lobed. In the latter case this characteristic determines the appearance of the tree crown.

In some species the first leaves produced by seedlings are of a different shape from those developed by an old plant and this may also occur when new branches grow. This is well seen in the Artocarpus where the juvenile leaves of seedlings are large and deeply lobed but where the leaves of the adult plant are much smaller and the margin is unserrated. By careful pruning, it might be possible to keep the attractive juvenile leaf on the plant for some time.

Leaves of any type may have their surfaces covered with tiny hairs or scales of many kinds in varying amounts. When very dense these coverings will completely alter the colour of the leaves and therefore the appearance of the true crown. Instead of hairs or scales, the leaf surface may be covered with a thin layer of wax and this usually makes it appear blue-green or grey-green in colour. Sometimes only the undersurface of the leaf has these coverings and the hairs or scales will change the colour to a whitish grey or brown, often giving it a shiny almost metallic appearance. In some species of trees and shrubs the leaves have no hairs or scales but the undersurface is deeply coloured pink, dark red or purple. With either kind, the effect of wind blowing through the trees is most attractive. The leaves give forth several changes in colour as the leaf undersurfaces flash. When the wind drops, the trees suddenly become entirely green again. The young leaves and flower buds of the Yellow Flame have a dense cover of short rusty brown hairs which drop away as the stem becomes older, and the silvery brown colour of durian leaves

Types of leaves

8

is due to the thin layer of tiny umbrella-shaped scales over their whole surface.

The shape and form of leaves will affect the general appearance of the tree. Some leaves are flat while others have upturned or undulating edges and others may be curved downwards. These characteristics in combination with the way the leaves are held on the twigs give the tree crowns a distinctive appearance.

Leaf shape is extremely variable and when it is to be used for identifying a tree, then the feature to look for is the general outline of the leaf, noting particularly where it is broadest. This may be in the middle, near the base or near the apex. The leaves may be long and narrow with parallel sides (linear), pointed towards both ends (lanceolate), oval (ovate), or broadest near the apex (obovate). The apex may be acute, obtuse or drawn out into a tip of varying lengths. The green colour of leaves shows a range of shades and this can be of use when selecting species for grouping as the variation in the colour provides much interest even though the leaves may be almost the same size. As mentioned previously, leaf colour can be modified by a covering of hairs, scales or wax, and in some species the leaf undersurface is strikingly different in colour from the upper surface. Some species have variegated leaves and there will be regular or irregular arrangements of white, yellow, pink, red, bronze or purple. These varieties are useful when planted as 'highlights' amongst trees with normal leaves, but too many of them are tiring to the eyes.

The majority of species have leaves in which the lamina is separated into two equal parts of the midrib and these are said to be symmetric. In

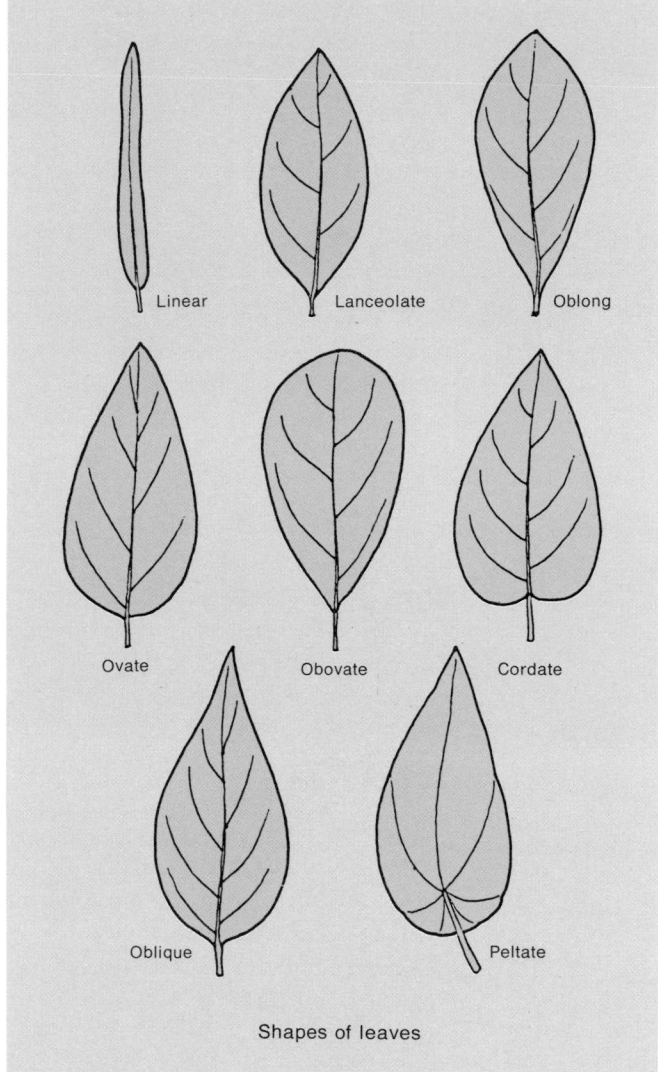

Shapes of leaves

some cases, however, the lamina is separated into two parts which are very unequal in size and these are said to be asymmetric.

The base of the lamina may be wedge-shaped (cuneate) or heart-shaped (cordate), or it may terminate abruptly with the margin at right angles to the leaf stalk. In a few cases, the leaf blade runs down on each side of the leaf stalk forming a narrow wing.

The veins in the leaf blade may be prominent or scarcely visible and the number and arrangement of the secondary veins are often helpful in

9

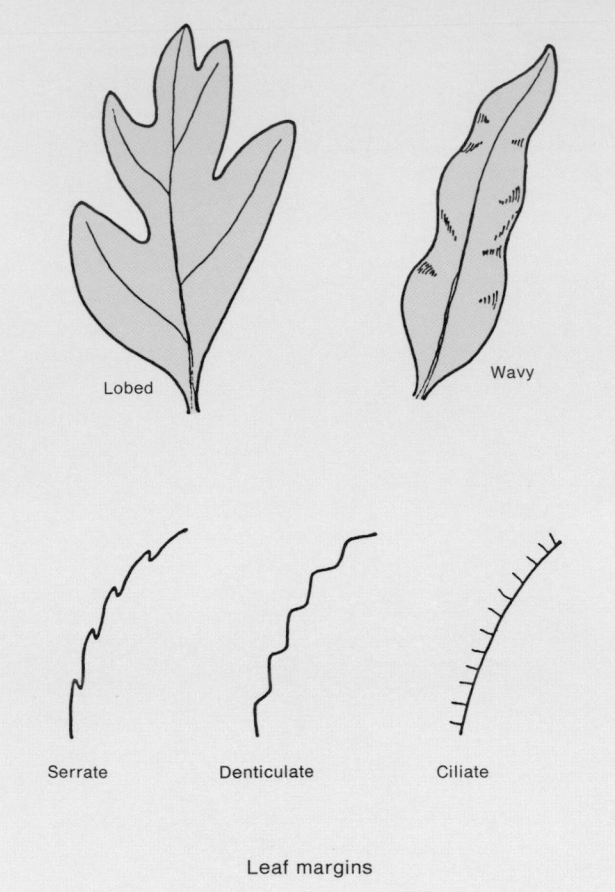

Lobed

Wavy

Serrate

Denticulate

Ciliate

Leaf margins

tripinnate. Leaflets of compound leaves have exactly the same variation in structure and shape as simple leaves and the same terms are used when describing them. Each leaflet may or may not have its own short stalk. Compound leaves with small leaflets usually impart a soft, feathery appearance to the tree as in the jacaranda and albizzia. If the leaflets are large then the appearance is similar to that of a species with small leaves. Palmate leaves when young, give a slightly formal effect; but as more of them develop and overlapping occurs the effect is lost.

In addition to the leaf shape and form, the arrangement of the leaves on the twigs will alter the appearance of the crown. The leaves may be spirally arranged all around the twigs or they may alternate when they appear in two rows, one on either side of each twig. Some species have corresponding pair of leaves on opposite sides of the stem. Should there be more than two leaves at each level, the arrangement is said to be whorled. With any of these arrangements close spacing of the leaves will give a dense crown, and wide spacing will give a sparse one.

identification. They are usually more easily seen in the lower surface of the leaf and sometimes are very prominent, being raised above the leaf surface. Very often, even though the veins are not raised above the leaf surfaces they are clearly seen because in many cases they are lighter in colour than the remainder of the leaf blade. The side veins may make a narrow or broad angle with the main vein and often are arranged at right angles to it.

Compound leaves are of two main kinds, the pinnate type having a single main rachis with leaflets spaced along it, and the palmate type in which all the leaflets are attached at one point. In some pinnate leaves the rachis may carry secondary branches, in which case, it is termed bipinnate. In a few species it may carry a third set of branches and is then termed

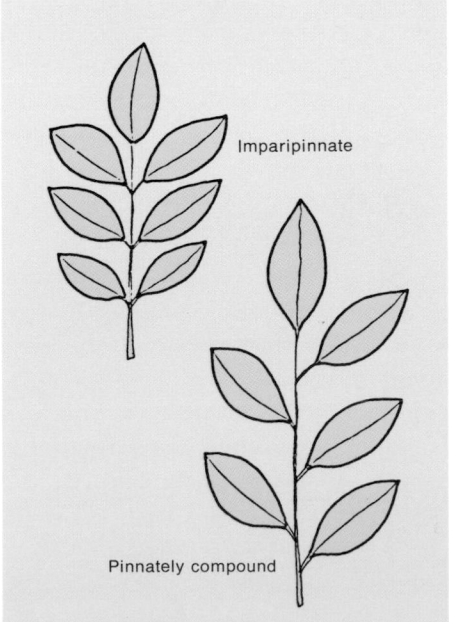

Imparipinnate

Pinnately compound

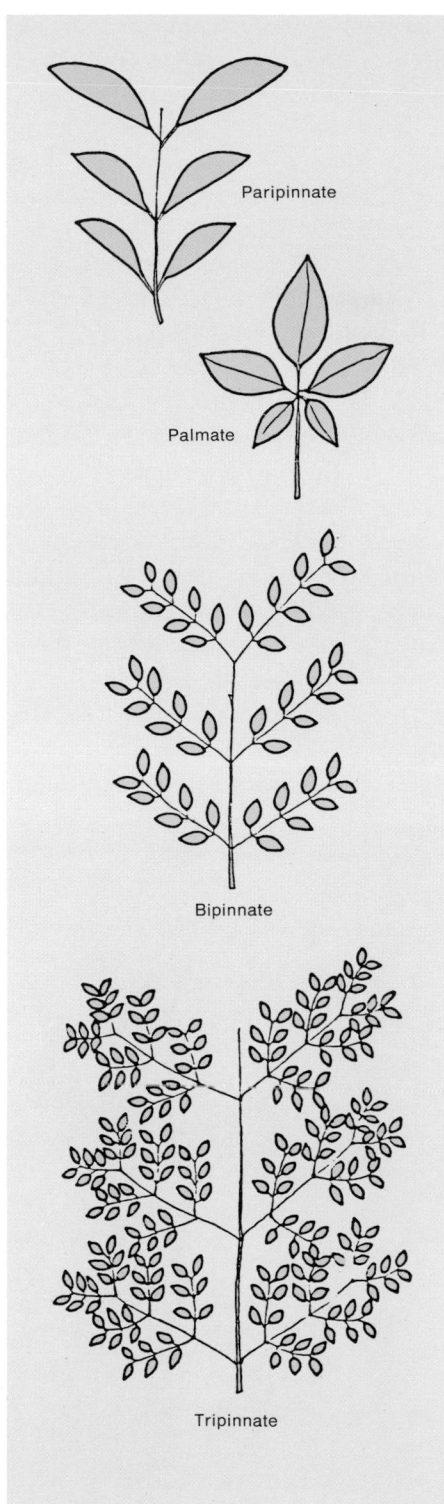

Paripinnate

Palmate

Bipinnate

Tripinnate

FLOWERS

Flowering of some species may occur almost throughout the year as in some of the species of cassia. Or it may occur only once or twice a year, usually in response to some change in weather conditions. Some trees produce flowers over the whole crown, whereas others may produce them only at the top of the crown. Many tropical trees have large, brightly coloured, conspicuous flowers in great proliferation. These may develop only at the tips of the twigs or they may arise along the twigs between the leaves. In a few cases, flowers develop directly on the trunk and main branches as in durian. Very often, single flowers are small and inconspicuous but are massed together in large in-florescences. These are sometimes produced while the tree is bare or while the new leaves are developing, so that there is less hindrance of pollination. Most of the ornamental flowering trees produce fruits, but in some cases they are unattractive and the trees are a little untidy until they have dropped. Other species have fruits of better shape and colour and these are an added attraction, making the trees, more interesting for a longer period. These species which flower at the tip of the crown can sometimes be planted at the base of a slope so that they can be viewed from above and the flowers can be better appreciated.

Some tree species produce large quantities of small fruits which can be attractive when they ripened. Unfortunately they are usually eaten by birds as soon as they are ripe. Planting such trees could be a means of encouraging birds to visit parks and other such places where desired.

BARK

Tree bark is often forgotten when a planting scheme is planned. In parks and gardens the trunks of trees can often be viewed at close range. There is a wide variety of texture, form and colour in tree barks and this can be made use of for decorative purposes.

Bark may be smooth, rough, flaky, or fissured. The colour ranges from pale grey to green, pale brown, dark brown and may be almost black. On older trees lichens grow on the bark and these are often only a few millimetres in height, but they form

circular, oval or maplike areas which are usually green, grey or white. Very often they produce many small fruiting bodies that are red or orange in colour. The lichens add considerably to the appearance of the bark. Trees with bark that is deeply fissured will often support a thick growth of epiphytic ferns and orchids. Many old rain trees show this feature very well. Tree trunks with smooth bark do not usually carry epiphytes. In some cases, the bark peels away in long strips and frequently the new young bark underneath shows a variety of coloration. Some eucalyptus trees have bark with pink, purple, pale green, mauve, cream and pale brown colours and are very attractive when looked at closely. There are some species of Tristania which are wild in the forest and these have peeling barks that are in shades

of reddish brown and brownish orange.

In all species, however, the bark will be dark coloured when wet, and if lichens are present they will often show up strikingly as they become pale green. Bark will be most attractive in appearance when it is dry and is a feature which should be remembered when planting trees in picnic areas and parks.

Trees

Trees may be grown for the beauty of their foliage or for their flowers and sometimes for both. In either case some trees are deciduous while others are evergreen. Deciduous trees generally lose their leaves once a year. In many species the whole crown of the tree is involved; but in other species only one or more branches drop their leaves, and this can make a tree look slightly untidy. The interval between leaf-fall and production of new leaves is variable and the new growth may begin within a few days or it may not occur for two to three weeks. Frequently the new, young leaves are brightly coloured pink, red or violet so that from a distance the tree appears to be in flower. As the young leaves mature they may become light green in colour and this gives the tree crown a light and airy appearance. Some of the deciduous trees produce their flowers while there are no leaves on the branches.

Evergreen trees produce new leaves at intervals and drop the older leaves gradually over a period of time. Often the new leaves and twigs develop rapidly and hang like tassels at the ends of the branches. These also may be brightly coloured and as they mature the twigs and leaves gradually assume their normal position.

Some of the ornamental trees produce flowers so abundantly that the whole crown of the tree is completely transformed for two or three weeks. In each case, this occurs once or twice a year only. But other species produce a smaller quantity of flowers, but over a longer period of time, and sometimes continuously. Some species produce flowers over the whole crown but others produce flowers only at the top of the crown so that they are not easily seen. Because of this the positioning of such species is important when planting.

A few trees are amenable to strong pruning and can be kept to a definite shape and size, but most will not tolerate too much pruning which can inhibit flowering.

Akasia Kuning, Wattle
Acacia auriculaeformis
LEGUMINOSAE

An evergreen tree of fast growth and producing a rounded crown. The density of the crown shows considerable variation but becomes thinner as the tree ages. The apparent 'leaves' are in fact, flattened leaf stalks called phyllodes. The tiny, yellow flowers are produced in short spikes in the leaf axils. The leaves drop continuously throughout the year. Propagated by seed and is not subject to attack by pests and diseases. Will grow on a variety of soils both inland and coastal and tolerates a wide range of soil conditions. The tree can be trimmed and will then make a useful, short screen.

Acacia cicinnata

A small tree five to seven metres high with light grey green phyllodes and an open, round crown. It is quick growing, relatively short-lived, and very effective when planted in front of trees with dark green foliage. Careful siting of single plants is necessary if the foliage is to show to the best advantage. The smaller yellow flowers are produced on very short axillary spikes.

Acacia mangium

This species makes a well-shaped tree of 10–15 metres with an oblong crown. The phyllodes are large and broad, and are dark green in colour. The crown is slightly open and the trees are quick growing. At intervals during the year white, fluffy flowers are produced in groups of spikes in the axils of the phyllodes. The tree has a solid appearance and can be planted singly or in groups.

Mata Kucing, Saga
Adenanthera pavonina
LEGUMINOSAE

A deciduous tree about 18 metres tall with irregular rounded crown and pale greyish brown bark. Leaves are large, bipinnate, up to 40 cm long with two to six pairs of secondary stalks. Each stalk carries 9–15 pairs of leaflets which are 30–45 cm long and 15–30 cm broad. Leaflets are oblong with blunt, rounded apex. The small cream coloured flowers are carried in axillary racemes and are followed by long, coiled pods up to 23 cm in length and 1.3 cm wide, each containing many bright scarlet, shiny seeds. Easily propagated from seeds. Grows well on most soil types and gives a light shade. Leaves are dropped once every year, and before new leaves develop there will be no shade.

Albizzia falcata
LEGUMINOSAE

Native to Sabah and Sarawak, this large, fast growing tree has smooth, pale grey bark. When mature it has a flat topped crown which is very characteristic because of the feathery appearance of the leaves. It is one of the fastest growing trees in the world and may reach 30 metres in about ten years with good growing conditions. The leaves may be up to 30 cm long with 8–12 pairs of secondary stalks which carry 15–18 pairs of leaflets about 1.3 cm by 1.3 cm broad. The small, cream coloured flowers are arranged in axillary panicles and have long, white stamens. The fruits are 12–15 cm long and 1.3–1.9 cm wide with numerous small, oval, pale brown seeds. Easily propagated from seeds. It will grow on most soils. It makes a striking specimen tree but because of the very rapid growth, the wood tends to be soft and after eight to ten years it begins to shed branches. Also the main roots often spread near the surface of the ground so that it is not recommended for car parks or public places. However, it can be used in a very large landscape design when it could be positioned to give a distinctive skyline.

Pulai

Alstonia augustifolia

APOCYNACEAE

A very tall tree up to 40 or 50 metres in height with grey bark. The narrow elliptic leaves are arranged in whorls of four to eight. The trees are deciduous, quick growing and the crown is oblong in young trees but open and irregular when old. Young trees have a layered appearance as the branches develop in whorls and are horizontal. It is probably best planted singly or in a small group.

Pride of Burma
Amherstia nobilis
LEGUMINOSAE

A medium sized evergreen tree with a slightly conical crown when young, but becoming rounded in older plants. The crown is very dense and becomes dotted with pendant racemes of pink flowers. The species is not very common and is suitable for a house garden or larger grounds. The young leaves appear simultaneously from a branch and hang limply downwards. These are pinkish green at first and change colour to green as they mature and as the stem becomes stronger.

Kelempayan, Bur Flower Tree

Anthocephalus cadamba
RUBIACEAE

A deciduous tree which can reach 30 metres and having a single, main trunk in which the branches are arranged stiffly and horizontally but with drooping tips. The ovate leaves are large and opposite, up to 30 cm long and 15 cm broad; larger in saplings with a short acute apex and heart-shaped base. They are drooping and have stalks up to four cm long. The small flowers are held in dense, stalked heads five cm wide which are terminal on short, side branches. The seeds are very tiny but germinate easily and the species would be interesting in a mixed group.

Araucaria bidwillii
ARAUCARIACEAE

An introduced plant which will reach 20 to 30 metres. It is conical with many branches and the secondary branches are long and drooping. The spirally arranged leaves are closely formed, lanceolate, and the apex is elongated to a long, stiff point. The plant is very susceptible to attack by termites and should be observed continuously so that control measures may be applied before any damage occurs. The species has a rather stiff appearance and can be planted singly or in mixed group of trees and shrubs.

Norfolk Pine
Araucaria excelsa
ARAUCARIACEAE

A tall tree of 30 or 40 metres in height with a conical shape and horizontal branches developed in whorls. The secondary branches may be horizontal or drooping and have a soft appearance because of the numerous, small, spirally arranged leaves. The leaves are one to two cm long and are curved inwards towards the stem. This species can be planted singly or in mixed groups and is also subject to damage by termites.

Cucur Atap

Baeckia frutescens

MYRTACEAE

A small tree up to six metres high which can be maintained also as a shrub. When well-grown it has an attractive, light and airy aspect because of the very small, narrow leaves. The ends of the slender branches are pendant, giving a drooping aspect. The small, white flowers are only about four mm wide and are inconspicuous. The species would be worth an attempt for bonsai work.

Tapak Kuda, Kupu Orchid Tree
Bauhinia blakeana
LEGUMINOSAE

A small tree which can reach six metres in height with a slender trunk and a rounded, open crown. The trees are evergreen, flower almost continuously and give light shade. They are suitable for small gardens or small, open areas near large buildings but must receive ample sunlight otherwise flowering will cease. Fruits are developed in some varieties but these have less attractive flowers. The flowers produce a very pleasant perfume.

Bottle-brush Tree
Callistemon sp.
MYRTACEAE

A small tree of up to eight metres in height with a stout trunk having fissured bark. When young the crown is open, but in older trees it becomes very dense and is round or oval in shape. The ends of the branches are drooping and the leaves are small, light green, narrow and lanceolate. They are spirally arranged on the branches. The flowers are produced in elongated spikes at the ends of the branches and the tips of the flower spikes later continue growth and produce leaves in the usual manner. Consequently the flower appears some way behind the branch tip; and, as they have long stamens giving them a fluffy appearance, they resemble a brush. This tree is best planted singly and prefers drier environment.

Penaga Laut
Calophyllum inophyllum
GUTTIFERAE

This is another tree originating from coastal areas but which is often planted inland for ornamental purposes. Mature trees have a dense crown with an irregular outline and are very handsome. They are evergreen with closely arrange dark green, thick, leathery leaves and flower once or twice a year. The flowers are white with a very strong, sweet fragrance and the fruits that develop later are small, round and green. These trees are easily grown from seeds but are slow in growth while young. The main branches often develop low on the trunk and interesting shapes result. The crown is oval while the tree is young.

Kenanga
Canagium odoratum
ANNONACEAE

An evergreen tree growing to about 12–16 metres in height although very old specimens may be much taller. The main branches and the secondary branches are pendant, especially near the tips, and this gives the tree a drooping appearance. Young trees have a conical crown but this becomes oval as the tree ages. Flowers are produced when the tree is quite young and they are green at first, changing to a dull yellow as they mature. The flowers are very fragrant and are often offered for sale in the market.

Rajah Kayu, Indian Laburnum

Cassia fistula
LEGUMINOSAE

A tree of up to nine metres high with a rounded oval crown. It is deciduous and loses its leaves about once a year. The flowers are produced on large hanging inflorescences at the same time as the new leaves are bright yellow. They are produced in great profusion and a tree in full flower is a very fine sight. Young plants will not flower and need constant attention as the leaves are badly attacked by insects. Older plants are less troubled by insects and the trees begin to flower at about four or five years of age. The leaves are pinnate with large, smooth leaflets. Propagation by seeds.

Kotek, Horse Cassia
Cassia grandis
LEGUMINOSAE

This is an introduced species and can grow to 16 or 18 metres in height with a round but irregular crown. The leaves are pinnate with very dark green leaflets which make the tree easy to recognize. It is deciduous and the pink flowers develop on the twigs before the new leaves appear. It can be planted singly or in groups with other tree species.

Johor, Kassod Tree
Cassia siamea
LEGUMINOSAE

Medium sized tree which may reach 18 metres in height with a rounded crown when young but becoming irregular in shape when older. This can be avoided by appropriate pruning. The leaves are evergreen, pinnate and dull green in colour. The pale, yellow flowers are produced in long, broad, terminal inflorescences which are somewhat untidy. They are followed by numerous long, flat, brown fruits which give the tree a ragged appearance. Propagation by seed or large cuttings.

33

Ru
Casuarina
CASUARINACEAE

Three species are grown and all have a formal appearance as they are without normal leaves as found in other trees. The work of the leaves is taken over by many numerous small, almost needlelike branches. Because of this structure, wind movement through these trees makes a good soothing sound. The smallest green branches live for a short time only and then drop, forming a thick mat around the base of the trunk. The trees, if overhanging a roof, can therefore cause clogging of drains and gutters. The commonest species is *Casuarina equisetifolia* which is normally found along sandy sea coasts but can be grown inland with equal success. There appears to be some variation between seedlings in the density of the crown. All species, when young, have a conical shape which is very attractive, but within two to four years the main branches develop more strongly and the conical

shape is lost. The roots develop very strongly after a few years and often push themselves above ground level. It is therefore prudent to plant casuarinas some distance from roads or levelled areas which need to remain flat. When young the trees are readily manageable and can be clipped into various shapes. Their size can then be controlled. Such treatment appears to delay the strong root development near the soil surface. Clipping must be started while the trees are very young otherwise they become too tall and the trunk becomes too large for such treatment to give an effective shape. Moreover new young branches will not develop.

Casuarina nobilis is much slower growing than the former species and the needle twigs are crowded near the branch tips so that the whole plant has a dense, soft, rounded shape and this is retained for many years. In older plant after the secondary branches have enlarged the tuft of needle twigs are only found on the smaller branches so that the crown becomes very open but is still very attractive especially when grown as a specimen tree.

Casuarina rumphiana (Weeping ru) is less well-known and has much finer needle twigs than either of the preceeding species. The twigs are crowded near the branch tips and are dark green and drooping. The species is slow growing and when old has an open crown with irregular main branches.

35

Buta-buta, Pong-pong
Cerbera manghas
APOCYNACEAE

A small or medium sized tree which will eventually grow to 12 metres but it can be kept to six metres by pruning. The crown is dense, and round at first but becomes oval and then cylindrical in shape. The large, dark green, shiny leaves are from 5–30 cm in length. Small panicles of white fragrant flowers are produced throughout the year and in each inflorescence from one to four fruits may develop. The fruits are an added attraction as they are large, oval and have a green, shiny surface. The crown of a young tree may be somewhat open until sufficient branches have developed. Flowering begins as soon as the plants are well established. Propagation is by seeds or cuttings and the trees grow best in sunshine.

Kayu Manis, Wild Cinnamon

Cinnamomum iners
LAURACEAE

This is an evergreen tree up to 20 metres high with a dense, round or oval crown and oblong, dull green leaves which are almost opposite in arrangement. The leaves have three main veins and when crushed smell faintly of cinnamon. The small flowers are borne in panicles up to 25 cm long. Young leaves are bright red or pink and change to green and pale green as they mature. Flowers are produced at the same time as the new leaves and are often so abundant that the whole crown of the tree is covered. New leaves develop twice or three times each year. The tree is quick growing and will quickly screen low buildings; it shapes itself and has a slightly formal appearance so that it can be planted singly, or in rows, or mixed planting.

Tree Fern
Cyathea
FILICALE

Although this is not a flowering plant it makes a most elegant addition to any planting scheme and is probably best planted in groups in a mixed planting. The species can reach ten metres in height with a crown of finely divided leaves and the top of an unbranched stem. The species is very effective in a skyline or at elevation. It is also very decorative planted in small valleys. There are both lowland and highland species.

Mempat
Cratoxylon formosum
HYPERICACEAE

A tree from 15 to 36 metres in height with an open, round or oval crown which is slightly spreading. The species is deciduous and on bare trees the pale, pink flowers develop in clusters along the twigs. It has small to medium sized leaves and gives light to medium shade as the crown is not very dense.

Semarak Api, Flame of the Forest
Delonix regia
LEGUMINOSAE

This is a flat topped tree up to 18 metres high with smooth, light grey bark. The large leaves are bipinnate with numerous small, light green leaflets, giving them a very delicate appearance. The trees are deciduous and the large, red flowers are produced at the same time as the new leaves near the ends of the branches. After flowering large, flattened, woody, black pods develop but these never cause the tree to look untidy. In

good soil the trees grow rapidly but in poor soil the growth is much slower and the characteristic shape of the crown takes much longer to develop. Usually a few very long, often slightly drooping branches develop which carry the leaves near the tips. At this stage the tree looks somewhat bare but side shoots develop along the branches eventually making the crown more bushy in appearance. This development can sometimes be helped by lightly pruning the long branches to encourage development of the laterals. The trees need strong sunlight to develop properly. Easily grown from seed.

Perah
Elateriospermum tapos
EUPHORBIACEAE

A fine tree eventually reaching 25–40 metres in height with a very dense crown which is conical at first and becomes round, oval or cylindric later. The thick leaves are narrow and oblong with acute apices and have long petioles. Newly developed leaves are deep pink and provide a surprising contrast with the dark green, mature foliage. This species is excellent for single planting and makes a very fine avenue.

Enterolobium cyclocarpum
LEGUMINOSAE

A very large tree with a flat-topped crown and smooth, light grey bark. The leaves are bipinnate with many tiny, dark green leaflets. It is deciduous and the small, white flowers are produced in globular heads after the new leaves have formed. This is a very fine tree for single planting but, when planted as an avenue in front of very large buildings would also make a striking sight. The fruits are large and very attractive. They are broad, flat, coiled pods which become dark brown when ripe. They can be polished after thorough drying and make interesting decorative articles.

Dedap
Erythrina
LEGUMINOSAE

Quick growing trees which are partly or completely deciduous and with short, woody spines on the trunk for which reason they may be used as a hedge plant.

Erythrina orientalis

A medium sized tree up to 15 metres in height usually found wild in coastal areas. The tree is deciduous and the leaves drop during the dry season in the first few months of each year. The scarlet flowers are produced abundantly at this time and later when the leaves develop. The crown is dense and rounded while young but tends to become umbrella shaped as the tree becomes older. The twigs are spiny. It is easily propagated from very large cuttings and the roots do not become troublesome by growing above the ground surface.

Erythrina var.

Smaller than *Erythrina orientalis* with leaflet slightly different in shape. Mostly cultivated and reaching three to four metres. It appears to flower almost continuously with internodes of three to four weeks without flowers. It can be propagated by marcotting.

Erythrina variegata

Leaflets with a broad yellow band bordering the main veins.

Jambu Laut, Sea Apple
Eugenia grandis
MYRTACEAE

Native to coastal areas of Malaysia, but also found profusely inland. It is a tall tree of up to 24 metres high with a dense, dark green, oblong crown of large leaves. It grows quickly when young and does not produce buttresses or surface roots. The rough, grey brown bark is slightly fissured. The broad, oval-shaped, oppositely arranged leaves have entire margins, and a pointed tip which turns downwards. The white flowers are produced in axillary and terminal inflorescences, each flower being about four cm wide. Many flowers develop in each inflorescence, forming a dense cluster which resembles a powder puff because of the long stamens. Quantities of nectar are produced and when the tree is in full flower, it is a fine sight with the many inflorescences closely and evenly distributed over the whole crown. The fruits are green when ripe and contain one seed which germinates easily. The bark is thick and enables the tree to withstand lallang fires.

Malabirah Cabbage Tree
Fagraea crenulata
LOGANIACEAE

Native to Malaysia and Indonesia, this evergreen tree will reach 21 metres in height and normally grows in swampy land. The crown will eventually be flat-topped, but younger specimens have a layered appearance because of the stiff branches arranged at widely spaced intervals on the main trunk. The leaves are very large and fleshy and are up to 30 cm long and 25 cm broad. Flowers are about 3.8 cm wide with cream petals and are carried in large terminal panicles about 35 cm long and broad. The oval fruits are about 2.5 cm long and many develop in each inflorescence which then beco- mes very conspicuous. The species is somewhat slow growing. Propagation from seeds. The tree would be useful for planting in very wet areas and is best viewed from a distance because of its stiff appearance and relatively few leaves.

Tembusu
Fagraea fragrans
LOGANIACEAE

Native to Malaysia and Indonesia. This evergreen species is slow growing but eventually will reach about 30 metres. The bark is dark brown and deeply fissured and the trunk is without buttresses. Because of the method of branching, the trees have a drooping appearance because the alternate branchlets carry the small leaves in close set groups and the weight causes them to bend downwards. The leaves are light green, elliptic in shape and tapered to each end. They are up to 13 cm long and five cm wide. The crown of the trees is usually thin and light although often very young specimens will have a dense crown. If the trees are left untouched when young, the leaf branches will often enlarge, bow near the ground and then turn upwards again. These branches are very decorative when they are fully grown because of their shapes. Flowers of this species are small, cream coloured, very fragrant and are carried in stalked axillary cluster about 7.5 cm wide. Each flower is only about two cm wide and is followed by a small berry half a cm wide which is orange or orange-red when ripe. When flowering occurs it is profuse and the whole surrounding area will be fragrant. Propagation by seeds, which should be separated and washed after removal from the fruit wall. Birds and bats eat the fruits greedily and if, at fruiting time, the dried droppings formed beneath the tree are collected, the seeds therein will germinate as easily. Seeds and seedlings are very small and initial growth is very slow. This species is good for single planting or group planting in large, open areas.

Ficus elastica
MORACEAE

A large, evergreen tree with shiny, dark green, leathery leaves 7.6–15.2 cm long and 3.8–7.6 cm broad. Young trees have larger leaves and the stalk is up to 7.6 cm long. There are many long buds at the ends of the branches and many aerial roots are produced from the trunk and main branches. The tree does not always attain a good shape but can be interesting, planted on its own, because of the aerial roots.

Ficus benjamina
MORACEAE

It is a large evergreen tree with a round or oval crown and branches with drooping ends. The leaves are up to 10.2 cm long and 5.1 cm broad, dark green and shiny on the upper surface and with a long acute apex. The small fruits are produced on the axils of the leaves and when ripe attract many birds.

It should not be planted near house drains as the root system is extensive and massive. Seedlings found in the wild often show a range of different shapes so that it would be wise to use cuttings from a tree having a desirable shape.

Ficus religiosa
MORACEAE

A medium to large sized deciduous tree with smooth, pale brown or partly grey bark. The leaves are heart-shaped, up to 17.8 cm long with a long stalk tip 1.3–3.8 cm in length. The leaf stalk is up to 12.7 cm long.

The species loses all the leaves at some stage and the new leaves develop almost immediately giving the crown of the tree a very delicate appearance as a result of the young foliage.

Ficus roxburghii
MORACEAE

This small tree has very large leaves and develop a dense hemispherical crown with branches bending to ground level. The leaves are dark green, broadly oval and are 30–50 cm in length and width. Young leaves are pinkish brown but some become pale

green which turns dark green. Fruiting begins after three or four years and great numbers of figs are produced near the base of the trunk. The tree will reach three to five metres in height and in exposed positions may be damaged by wind as the large leaves are very heavy and are easily snapped. It grows easily from very large cuttings and is excellent for courtyard planting, or as a single plant. Small groups of it make a very impressive sight. The plant can be severely pruned and will soon produce new shoots.

Firmiana fulgens

This is a less well-known deciduous tree which can reach 18.3 metres in height and usually found growing in riverbanks. The crown is open and irregular and the trunk develops buttresses. The leaves are broad and elliptic and are often three-lobed. They have a heart shape base and an elongated tip, and a long stalk. The bright orange, hairy flowers are borne in clusters near the ends of the twigs after the leaves have dropped from the tree. The tree will remain bare of leaves for six to eight weeks. The fruits are also attractive as they are thin, papery, and boat-shaped with one or two seeds on the margin near the point of attachment. Propagated from seed. In cultivation some trees seem to retain their leaves throughout the year and consequently no flowers are produced.

Randa
Gardenia carinata
RUBIACEAE

This species is a small tree which may reach 14 metres. The crown is round or oval and is very open. Most parts of the plant are covered with fine hairs. The leaves can reach 35 cm in length and 15 cm in width but often are smaller than this. The large flowers are borne singly in the leaf axils and are about 12 cm wide and six to eight cm long. When they first open they are pale cream but become deep orange-yellow as they age. They have a strong fragrance. The fruits are oval, green at first and then yellow. The species is easily grown from seed and is useful for single planting or in groups, or in small avenues.

Mexican Lilac
Gliricidia sepium (maculata)
LEGUMINOSAE

A small to medium sized tree up to ten metres high with an open irregular crown when young. Old trees develop a large trunk and a crown which is rounded or slightly mushroom-shaped. When young, the tree can be very straggly unless it is pruned to encourage branching. Branches tend to develop near the base of the trunk and these should be cut away as they enlarge quickly and then are unsightly in appearance. The species is very vigorous and recovers easily from drastic pruning or cutting back. The leaflets are relatively small and the leaves droop during dry season. The tree then flowers on the twigs and bare branches. The racemes of pink flowers are produced abundantly and are followed by many thin, dry pods which split open and fall from the tree on dry days. Young trees give very light shade but large, old specimens give good shade. The roots are not aggressive and the tree can be propagated very easily by taking fairly large cuttings.

Gustavia superba
LECYTHIDACEAE

This species is a small tree up to three metres in height with a hemispherical or round, very dense crown. The large leaves are long, broad and lanceolate with toothed

margins. The young leaves are pinkish bronze but very quickly become dark green and shiny. The flowers are very large with many long white petals, numerous white stamens and have a strong, sweet smell. Each flower is 10–15 cm in diameter and the fruits are hemispherical with a flat top. The species can be planted singly, or in groups, or can be used for screening low buildings since it retains the lower branches.

Baru-baru, Sea Hibiscus
Hibiscus tiliaceus
MALVACEAE

Found throughout the tropics on seashores. This is a small tree with a round crown and dark green foliage. The leaves are 7.5–15 cm in diameter, heart-shaped and with an acute apex. They are glabrous on the upper surface but the undersurface may be hairy and white or glaucous. The flowers are carried sparsely branched on terminal and axillary inflorescences. They are about ten cm in diameter, bright yellow with a dark red base. The petals change colour to orangy pink when they open and fall. The fruit is a capsule, round or oval with the persistent calyx. Propagation by seeds. A good, small tree for planting near pathways or as a screen.

Lokus, West Indian Locust Tree

Hymenaea courboril

LEGUMINOSAE

A very tall tree with a smooth, round trunk up to 30 metres high. The crown is rounded, moderately dense with dark green shiny leaves.

Flowers are white but relatively inconspicuous and are followed by short thick rounded brown pods which have a strong smell when cut open. As the pods are hard and heavy the trees should not be used in car parks but for a large landscape effect as in golf courses or parks it is a very handsome tree. Grown from seeds.

Jambul Merak
Jacaranda filicifolia
BIGNONIACEAE

A small tree eventually reaching about 12 metres in height with a light, feathery appearance as the leaves are made up of a large number of very small leaflets. The crown is irregular and somewhat open but young plants tend to remain unbranched for a long time and often reach two to three metres before branching commences. In the climate of this country the blue or lilac flowers appear in clusters along the bare branches. Individual trees show some variation in the crown shape.

considerable differences and ranges from very dark green through paler green to blue green. The blue green forms are much prized and are exceedingly attractive. The species retain their branches close to the ground and although there are a number of main branches the whole outline of each tree remains conical. When these species become very tall they can become misshapen because

Juniper
Juniperus
CUPRESSACEAE

These plants are commonly used to give a formal effect as most of the varieties have a well-defined conical shape. The crown of these trees is very dense and the branches are covered with very small, almost scale-like leaves. They do not produce flowers but the colour of the foliage shows

of bending by high winds and heavy rain.

There are available some prostrate varieties which can be grown in pots or in rock gardens. These varieties need some attention to prevent new shoots from growing vertically as that would destroy the characteristic of the plant. Vertical shoots should be removed or should be wired into a horizontal position until they have matured.

Bungur

Lagerstroemia floribunda

LYTHRACEAE

Native to Burma, Thailand and Peninsular Malaysia. This species is a medium sized evergreen tree which will reach 18 metres, although under cultivation it is usually much shorter. The crown is dense and ranges from slightly conical to oval or cylindrical. The trunk is fluted at the base and the light brown bark is fleshy, falling away in thin oblong pieces. The leaves which are dull dark green measures 10–25 cm long and five to ten cm wide, and are oblong with a blunt apex and rounded base. The flowers are carried on panicles up to 40 cm long. Each flower is about 2.5 cm wide with pink or pale purple petals which turn to white as they age. Many small woody fruits develop in each panicle, oblong in shape and containing many small, dark brown seeds. Propagation by seeds is easy. This is a suitable tree for single or group planting as it flowers at intervals throughout the year. In gardens it seems to remain at about 4.5–6 metres in height and does not then cause much overshadowing of the surrounding plants and buildings.

Bungur, Rose of India
Lagerstroemia speciosa
LYTHRACEAE

Native to the lands from India to Australia. This well-known and commonly grown tree is partly deciduous and has a round or oval crown which will reach 15 to 24 metres high under cultivation. The bark is brownish grey and rough in texture. The leaves are up to 25 cm long and ten cm broad with a rounded base and blunt apex. They become red at withering before leaf-fall. Flowers are large and showy, carried in terminal upright panicles. Each flower will be up to six cm in diameter. The petals in the wild species are mauve in colour, but are pink in those under cultivation as these have undergone selection and are in fact new varieties. The flowers are followed by woody, dark brown oblong capsules containing many small, brown, winged seeds. Propagation is by seeds or marcotting. This is an excellent ornamental tree, but when young it is subject to considerable leaf damage by insect pests.

Gelam, Cajeput
Melaleuca leucadendron
MYRTACEAE

When well-grown this is a tree up to 24 metres high with a narrow, oval, grey-green crown which may be dense or slightly open. The bark is flaky and whitish or pale grey in colour and the main trunk appears twisted. The lanceolated leaves are 5–13 cm long and 1.3–3.8 cm wide with a short stalk. They are leathery in texture and have an acute apex. The white flowers with long stamens are arranged in spikes up to 15 cm long terminating in a bud which will produce another leafy shoot. The twigs therefore often show the small woody knob like fruits in the older portions, and leaves and flowers on the younger terminal portion. The plant is native of the Southeast Asian archipelago, including Malaysia and grows commonly in swampy areas. Under cultivation it will tolerate drier soil and can be grown inland as well. The bark is thick and enables it to withstand lallang fires.

Sentang
Melia excelsa
MELIACEAE

The species is wild in Peninsular Malaysia. It is a fine, tall, evergreen tree which will reach 45 metres. But under cultivation it may attain only 15–18 metres. The crown is oblong or oval and in young trees is very dense, but in older trees, it becomes more open. The bark is smooth and brownish grey in young trees and becomes fissured in older ones. There are no buttresses at the base of the trunk. The leaves are pinnate, up to 75 cm long, with 7–12 pairs of leaflets. Each leaflet can be up to 12 cm long and 3.8 cm wide with an asymmetric base, entire margin and a rather blunt apex. The leaves near the tops of the branches are held stiffly and give the tree a very characteristic outline. Large panicles of small, fragrant flowers are produced and followed by single seeded indehiscent fruit about 3.8 cm long. Propagation is easy from seed, which will grow in most types of soil. Good for shade and may be grown singly or in groups.

Mambu, Nim Tree, Margosa Tree
Melia indica
MELIACEAE

A small to medium sized evergreen tree with a round crown. In some tropical areas with a more seasonal climate it can form a very large tree. The pinnate leaves are up to 35 cm long with lanceolate, toothed leaflets which are asymmetric at the base. Each leaflet is curved away from the main leaf axis. The small, white flowers are carried in axillary panicles which are 30 cm long. These are followed by small, oblong fruits not more than 1.9 cm long which are yellow when ripe. Propagated by seeds. Not suitable for very small gardens.

Penaga, Ironwood Tree
Mesua ferrea
GUTTIFERAE

A slow growing, very handsome tree having both attractive foliage and flowers. It has a very dense crown which is conical when young and only loses its shape after many years when it changes to an oval or oblong shape. The lanceolate leaves are dark green on the upper surface and whitish green below so that the undersurface shows up conspicuously when the leaves move in the wind. The flowers are very large, 10–15 cm in diameter, with white petals and many bright yellow stamens and are produced abundantly about twice each year. This fine tree can be planted singly, in groups or as an avenue and would be excellent near buildings as a mature tree has a very solid appearance because of the density of the crown.

flower. The fruits are greyish brown and when ripe they split open to release the small, black seeds covered in a thin, red pulp to dry out on slender, white strings. Crown sometimes thin. Propagation by seeds or marcotting. Its scented flowers in smaller gardens make it especially appealing.

Cempaka Merah
Michaelia champaka
MAGNOLIACEAE

Native to India and Malaysia. Similar to Michaelia alba but smaller in size and with leaves more yellow than green in colour. The flower petals are yellow and orange in colour and many fruits are developed. Each fruit is made up of several separate fruitlets developed from a single

Jeneris
Milletia atropurpurea
LEGUMINOSAE

A slow growing tree eventually reaching 24–30 metres, although most specimens are much shorter. It is an evergreen tree with a very dense, round or cylindrical crown and giving a deep shade. The leaves are a mass of dark green, shiny leaflets and the tree always has a neat and well-groomed appearance. Flowering occurs after dry weather and the crown of the tree is then dotted with large, very dense inflorescences of dark purple flowers. Fruits are large and brown in colour when ripe, somewhat irregular in shape. Propagation is easy from seed. Root growth is no problem with the species.

Tanjung
Mimusops elengi
SAPOTACEAE

This is a well-known tree native to India, Sri Lanka (Ceylon) and Burma and introduced throughout the tropics. It is an evergreen tree with a round, dense, dark green crown which always retain a neat appearance. The leaves are leathery, oblong with an acute apex, wavy with upturned edges and can reach 15 cm long by 7.5 cm wide. The small fragrant white flowers are produced in small groups in the leaf axils. Small oval fruits 2.5 cm long are produced and are orange when ripe. Easily propagated by seed.

Mengkudu
Morinda citrifolia
RUBIACEAE

A small evergreen tree with a conical crown. It can grow to nine metres in height. The whole plant is glabrous and the glossy, dark green leaves are up to 30 cm by 15 cm. They are elliptic with an acute apex and have large stipules at the base of the stalk. The flowers are carried in heads and the calyx tubes are joined. Consequently, the fruit is a multiple structure made up of the fruits from separate flowers which are joined together by the fleshy calyces. The whole structure appears like a greyish white potato. Easily grown from seeds.

Japanese Cherry
Muntingia calabura
TILIACEAE

A common, small tree introduced from tropical America, it spreads rapidly by tiny seeds. The tree is evergreen with a dense, spreading, often umbrella-shaped, crown which sometimes has a layered appearance. The leaves can be up to 13.7 cm long and 5.1 cm wide, and are ovate although narrow, and have an asymmetric base. They are alternate and have toothed margins. The flowers are white, about 2.5 cm in diameter and rise singly or in groups of three on the leaf axils. The fruits are small, red berries containing numerous tiny seeds. The species is attractive when planted where it can be viewed from above or it can be used in small areas where larger trees are unsuitable to create a park like effect. Groups of three or five specimens are very decorative.

Taban Putih, White Gutta
Palaquium obovatum
SAPOTACEAE

A fine medium to large tree up to 36 metres high with an oblong or cylindrical crown. The leaves are spirally arranged on fairly large twigs and are obovate, dark green on the upper surface and slightly greyish green on the undersurface. Young leaves are light green and are held stiffly on the twigs, resembling small, green candles. The main, lower branches often produce the secondary branches in one plane so that the lower parts of the crown have a slightly layered appearance. This species is good for planting in small groups and will tolerate some shade.

Screw Pine
Pandanus
PANDANACEAE

These are large plants producing many strong thick roots for some distance up the stem above ground level. Several species are available but the one which is most commonly grown is that which has variegated leaves. A single plant may reach six metres in height and six metres in diameter. The leaves are long and hard, with spines on the edges and main veins so that it is not suitable for planting too close to public pathways. It makes a magnificent specimen plant or can be used at the back of a large, mixed group of plants. Sometimes shoots with entirely green leaves are produced. These should be removed immediately as they will never develop variegated leaves.

Batai, Yellow Flame
Peltophorum pterocarpum
LEGUMINOSAE

A tall, quick growing tree with a rounded, slightly flattened crown and reaching 24 metres in height. The large, dark green leaves are bipinnate and deciduous. New shoots begin to develop about one week after the leaves have dropped and are covered with a dense, dark golden brown coat of hairs. The inflorescences are terminal on the new shoots and are panicles of large, bright yellow flowers. Flowering is abundant and the tree is highly ornamental. The flowers are followed by thin, purple brown pods which are also attractive in appearance. Grown from seeds.

Madras Thorn
Pithecellobium dulce
LEGUMINOSAE

Native to tropical America but introduced to all parts of the tropics. Evergreen, small or medium sized tree which will reach 12–15 metres high. It is easily recognized by the greyish green colour of the small leaflets. The crown may be rounded but can also become irregular in shape by the development of large secondary branches. Small, hard spines are present in all branches and persist sometimes on the larger branches and trunk. The leaves are small with one pair of side stalks which carry two leaflets each. The branch is about 30 cm long and the leaflets are asymmetric, 2.5–5 cm long by 0.6–1.9 cm wide. The small greenish flowers are carried in heads on a long open terminal panicle which may be up to 4.5 metres long. The pods when matured are coiled and about 1.3 cm thick containing several black seeds. Each seed is covered by a pink and white pulp which is eaten greedily by birds. Propagation is easily carried out from seeds. The species can be used to create a light screen and it can also be trimmed to keep it to any particular size. It makes a good hedge and as it is thorny it prevents people and animals from making pathways through it.

Pine
Pinus caribaea
PINACEAE

These are the true pine trees and two or three species are available for planting. They have decorative bark and foliage and often produce cones. In general, they retain a conical shape even when matured and the long, needle-like leaves are quite distinctive in appearance. These trees are easy to grow but can be very susceptible to attack by white ants. A well grown specimen is decorative on its own but it is probably better to plant them in small groups.

Saga Gajah
Pithecellobium ellipticum
LEGUMINOSAE

Native to Malaysia. This evergreen tree will eventually attain 18 metres but in cultivation reach 9–12 metres only. The crown is oblong and the large bipinnate leaves make it very dense. Each leaf has two pairs of side stalks with two to four pairs of leaflets on the upper side stalk and one to two pairs on the lower side stalk. The stalks varies from 12–30 cm in length and the leaflets on the upper side stalk are 12–30 cm long by 5–15 cm wide. The flowers are small and inconspicuous and are carried on loose terminal and axillary panicles up to 50 cm in length. The pods are broad and strongly twisted, becoming dull red when ripe and after dehiscence the large black seeds hang out on short stalks from the pods. Propagation by seeds. The tree is useful for small areas or for mixing with other trees to give variation in height and leaf form.

Kemboja, Frangipanni

Plumeria obtusa
Plumeria acuta
Plumeria rubra
APOCYNACEAE

All species are small trees with very thick, stout branches. The spirally arranged leaves are held near the ends of the branches. When leaves or branches are cut, a large quantity of white latex drains out of the cut surfaces for several minutes. Two species have white flowers and the third has pink or red flowers. All are fragrant.

Jati Laut, Sea Teak
Podocarpus polystachyos
PODOCARPACEAE

This tree is native to Malaysia and is found wild in coastal areas. The crown is conical when young but becomes irregular in shape as the tree ages. It is slow growing with short linear, dark green, shiny leaves and will tolerate pruning. When young the branches are sometimes drooping but becomes horizontal as they mature. Pruning encourages branching and the species would make an excellent broad, dense hedge. Young leaves are pale green and make a pleasing contrast with the dark green of the matured leaves.

Podocarpus rumphii
PODOCARPACEAE

A slow growing tree with narrow, linear, dark green, shiny leaves. The crown is conical when young and becomes oval or oblong as it becomes older. It always has a neat appearance and is suitable for planting singly or in groups, but is useful also in mixed groups of species.

Polyalthia longifolia
ANNONACEAE

This is a very handsome conical tree with shiny, dark green leaves having very wavy margins. The leaves are long and lanceolate while the flowers are greenish, inconspicuous and borne on the older parts of the twigs. The species can be planted singly or in groups or can be used to make a fine avenue. The conical shape is retained for many years until some of the lower branches become larger and the crown then becomes irregular.

Pometia pinnata

A common riverside tree which can reach 30 metres and which develops large buttresses at the base of the trunk. It is evergreen with very large pinnate leaves which has no terminal leaflet and all parts of the plant are glabrous except the inflorescence. On an adult plant each leaf will have three to six pairs of leaflets but in saplings there will be up to 16 pairs. Leaflets can be up to 35.5 cm long and 15.2 cm wide and are oblong with an acute apex and toothed margin. The tiny flowers are developed on very large inflorescence up to 60.9 cm long and later carry black fruits which are up to 3.8 cm long. The tree develops an open irregular crown and new, young leaves are bright red. It is easily propagated from seed.

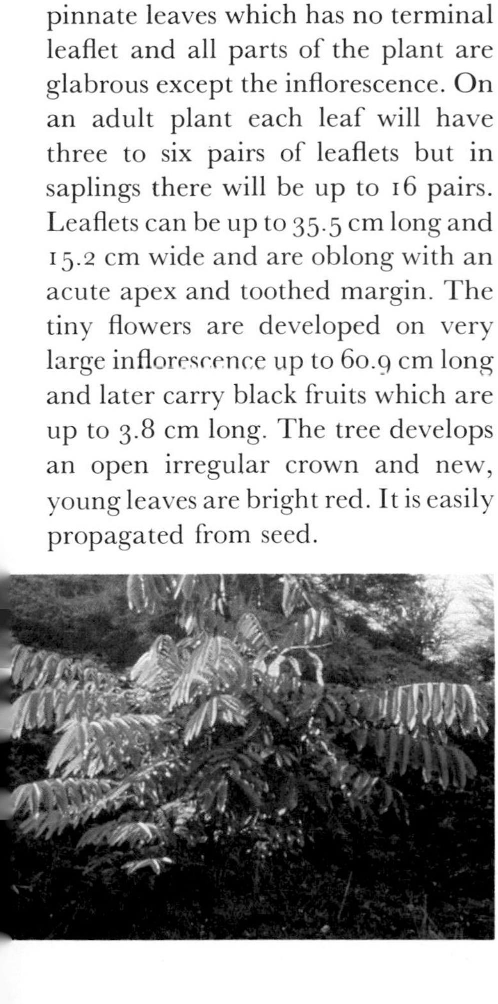

Mempari
Pongamia pinnata
LEGUMINOSAE

This is a wild species of the coastal areas in this country. It is deciduous and will eventually grow to about 20 metres high. It has a dense, round crown and pinnate leaves with dark green, shiny leaflets. The leaves are up to 30 cm long with two or three pairs of leaflets. The pale, pink flowers are produced when the new leaves are developing. Easily propagated from seeds.

Sial Menahun
Pternandra echinata
MELASTOMACEAE

Native to Malaysia. A small tree with a round crown and growing at six to nine metres in height. The twigs are slender and slightly drooping, giving the tree a very graceful effect. The simple leaves are oblong with a long acute apex and are up to 12 cm long by 3.8 cm wide. The leaf stalk is very short, and the leaves are oppositely arranged. Flowers are borne in small groups of two to four at the ends of the branches and are about 1.9–2.5 cm in diameter with pale blue or white petals. The small hemispherical fruits are covered with soft, green spines. Propagation by seed or marcotting. Useful in areas where dark foliage would be gloomy or it could be used effectively for single planting, group planting or along paths.

Sena, Angsana
Pterocarpus indicus
LEGUMINOSAE

A very fine, large deciduous tree up to 30 metres high with a cylindric or dome shaped crown with very drooping lower branches and upper branches less so. The tree gives good shade and the trunk develops large buttresses at the base as it becomes older. The roots tend to rise above ground level near the trunk and as the leaves drop once each year, sweeping up of fallen leaves would be necessary in parks or small areas. The trees may be cut back and new branches will grow very rapidly but the crown shape will then tend to be cylindrical. The trees flower after the leaves are fully developed and the whole crown of the tree will be covered with light yellow, scented flowers. The petals drop very quickly, making an attractive yellow carpet underneath the tree. In some parts of the country all the leaves will fall at about the same time but in other areas the leaves shed slowly from the bottom of the crown upwards. In the former case new leaves appear from the base of the crown upwards. There may also be some variations between seedling stocks. A group of these trees may show considerable variation in the time of leaf fall so that the general appearance of the groups as a whole would be rugged. This might be avoided by taking cuttings from one tree only for use in group planting. All the trees in such a group would then lose their leaves at the same time and would develop new leaves at the same time, resulting in a considerable improvement in appearance. Propagation is easy from seed or by means of large cuttings.

Willow
Salix sp.
SALICACEAE

A small, slender tree with arching branches and a thin, open crown. The small, narrow, light green leaves are sometimes drooping and are 7–15 cm long. An introduced species grown for ornamental purposes only. Badly attacked by leaf-eating insects when young. Propagated by cuttings.

Pukul Lima, Rain Tree
Samanea saman
LEGUMINOSAE

Native to tropical America and introduced to Malaysia. A deciduous tree up to 24 metres high with a very characteristic flat-topped crown. It is wide spreading, fast growing initially and the main roots spread and enlarge near the soil surface. The leaves are bipinnate with three to six pairs of side stalks bearing six to eight pairs of large, dark green leaflets on the upper side stalks. Leaflets near the end of the side stalks are larger than those near the lower portion and vary from oblong to almost diamond shaped (rhomboid). Flowers are borne on heads about 7.5 cm wide and are developed in groups up to five in number on the axils of the younger leaves. The flowers are pink and white but only the central flower of one head will form a fruit. The pods are up to 25 cm long, dark brown or black containing many brown seeds about one and 1.3 cm long embedded in brown pulp. The leaflets close up at night or during heavy rain. Propagated by seeds and will grow on most soils. When older the branches

usually support a dense growth of epiphytes giving the tree a comfortable and long established appearance. It makes a good specimen tree and can be used for avenue planting provided it is not planted too near a road edge because of the root system.

Saraca indica
LEGUMINOSAE

An introduced species which is a small tree with pinnate leaves having large lanceolate leaflets. The small flowers are borne in clusters on the ends of the branches. The stems of the inflorescence are purple and the flowers are pale orange when they open, becoming dark orange red as they age. The crown of the tree is irregular and somewhat open.

Yellow Saraca
Saraca thaipingensis
LEGUMINOSAE

A small to medium sized evergreen tree six to nine metres high. The large pinnate leaves have five to eight pairs of large leaflets and a very short stalk. The species is native to this country and grows alongside streams in the forest with their roots often trailing in the water. When cultivated they do well in shaded damp areas which do not become waterlogged. New leaves develop several times each year and the young shoots grow rapidly forming a tassel of pink or purple leaves at the ends of the branches. The new leaves assume the normal green colour and the leaf stalks their usual alignment within a short time. The flowers are produced in large inflorescences on the trunk and main branches. The inflorescence has yellow branches of bracts and flowers. A number of large, thin, flat purple pods come eventually. They are very striking in appearance. Propagated from seeds.

Potato Tree

Solanum wrightii

SOLANACEAE

A coarse, evergreen, small tree of up to 12 metres high with large pinnately lobed leaves which often bear thorns. All parts of the plant are covered with coarse hairs. Each leaf can be up to 30 cm long and 18 cm wide. The large flowers are produced continuously in small inflorescences which appear to arise on the stem and not at the axils of leaves. Each flower is six cm in diameter, deep violet when newly opened and fades to white within a few days. There is a bright yellow core of stamens in the centre of each flower. The fruits are globular and about five cm in diameter, become orange yellow when ripe. The species originated in South America and commonly cultivated. Propagated easily from seed. Can be planted singly or in groups.

Pancut, African Tulip Tree
Spathodea campanulata
BIGNONIACEAE

Fast growing tree, flowering when very young but with wide spreading roots and soft wood. The tree will reach 21 metres in height and as it becomes older the trunk develops small buttresses at the base. The pinnate leaves have 10–16 large, coarse leaflets which are dark green in colour. The crown is irregular because of the method of branching. When young the crown tends to be oval in shape and very young plants do not branch until they have become 2.5–3 metres high. The flowers are large and red with yellow border to the petals. They are seen best when the trees have been planted below eye level, as the inflorescences are produced over the top of the tree crown. Fruits often develop and are large, black, spear-shaped structures which split open, releasing many small, winged seeds. Propagated by seed.

Kelumpang Burung
Sterculia parviflora
STERULIACEAE

A deciduous species reaching 16
metres with brownish grey, flaky
bark. The leaves are ovate to oblong
with short acute apex and a rounded
base. They range from 10–28 cm in
length and are up to 15 cm wide. The
small inconspicuous flowers are
borne in pendulous racemes and give
rise to large pods 10–15 cm in length
and width. The surface of the pods is
velvety and becomes brilliant red
when mature. When ripe, they split
open and the blue black, oval seeds
hang outside the fruit on short stalks.
The crown of the tree is dense and is
slightly conical at first becoming oval
or oblong as the tree becomes older.
The foliage retains a light, fresh green
colour for a long time.

Broad-leafed Mahogany
Swietenia macrophylla
MELIACEAE

This deciduous species will eventually grow into a large tree and when young has a dense, dark green, oval crown, but as it becomes older the crown often becomes more open and irregular in shape. Older trees will show small buttresses and the bark is brownish grey with ridges and fissures. Leaves range from 20 to 50 cm in length with three to six pairs of large leaflets which show considerable difference in size in each leaf. Those near the tip of the leaf are larger than those near the base. Leaflets are from

10–18 cm long and 2.5–7.5 cm broad, elliptic, asymmetric and are curved. The small, greenish yellow flowers are carried in axillary panicles which are shorter than the leaves. They develop as the new leaves appear. The fruits are large, woody capsules up to one-and-a-half cm long with dark brown, winged seeds attached by their wing tips to a central stalk. These are blown away by the wind. Propagation is by seeds and young plants tend to grow without branching until they have reached about five to six metres. Lateral branches then develop and upward growth is slowed considerably. Not suitable for car parks but excellent for group planting in large open areas.

Tabebuiea rosea
BIGNONIACEAE

This tree really needs a more seasonal climate than is available in Malaysia and might flower better in the northern part of the country for this reason. However, it grows quite well elsewhere and makes a small tree with well spaced branches and an open oval or cylindric crown. It has large, pinnate leaves and normally is deciduous, flowering while the branches are bare. In this climate, flowers develop while the leaves are still on the tree. They develop in clusters and are large and pale pink in colour.

Ketapang, Sea Almond
Terminalia catappa
COMBRETACEAE

This is a very common tree which is found wild in coastal areas. It is quick growing and consequently is often planted as a shade tree but it loses its leaves twice a year. As the leaves are large they need to be swept away otherwise the area around the tree base becomes very untidy. It has a very characteristic shape when young as the branches grow out from the main trunk, giving the plant a layered appearance. The branches are held stiffly, almost at right angles to the trunk and the large leaves are arranged closely together near the branch tips. Before falling, the leaves become red or yellow. Leaf-fall does not commence until the trees are approximately four years old. It flowers and fruits abundantly. After fruiting, seedlings may be found everywhere as bats eat the outer covering of the fruits and drop the seed. Older plants lose the layered appearance as one of the lateral branches becomes larger and the tree then develops an irregular crown. Young trees 10–14 metres high are commonly seen. Older ones may reach 28 metres. The crown is dense and the branches tend to droop at the tips.

Yellow Oleander
Thevetia peruviana
APOCYNACEAE

A small tree with round or oval crown if unpruned and with relatively small branches. The long narrow leaves are held close together along the branches and give the tree a soft appearance. Yellow trumpet shaped flowers are produced throughout the year and these are followed by broad pale green fruits containing a single large seed. There are cultivars with white flowers and orange flowers, but both are similar in habit to the yellow flower kind. The tree is easily propagated from cuttings and may be used to create a thin screen or a fast growing hedge. By suitable pruning it can be kept to any required height.

Tree of Life
Thuja
CUPPRESSACEAE

This is another genus of dark green, conically shaped trees which do not produce flowers. The branches are densely covered with small scale-like leaves and are arranged on one plane, each group of branches being held vertically. This gives the species a very distinctive appearance which is slightly less formal than that of Juniperus.

Fruit Trees

Malaysia is well-known for her tropical plant species. In terms of edible fruits there are hundreds of tropical fruits different in form, flavour, fragrance and size. Most of our local fruits are seasonal except for papaya and star fruit. Fruits like durian, rambutan, mangosteen, duku, langsat are found in localized areas at certain time of the year.

Most of the fruit trees are found in the rural areas of mixed farming in kampungs and villages and at times in orchards ranging from one to 200 hectares. Hence the beauty of the fruit trees as an ornamental tree is often not realized and not appreciated. Nowadays fruit trees are becoming more common in the urban areas and housing estates. It is common now to see a fruit tree in the compound of each house. Fruit trees like durian, nangka or jackfruit, rambutan and mangoes are the most commonly grown trees in the urban areas. Fruit trees are useful not only as a source of vitamins for our own consumption but they can also help to beautify our surroundings and improve the scene of a concrete jungle so prevalent in housing development. Beside supplying us with fruits, fruit trees have also become an ornamental plant and should be made use of more. Many of the fruit trees have beautiful shapes and a shady canopy. They flower and set fruits which are equally attractive, thus providing additional colour and fragrance to the environment.

Fruit trees growing in the jungle behave quite differently once they are domesticated. They are propagated by different techniques such as marcotting, grafting and inarching. Thus the progenies of trees obtained behave differently and take different shapes when grown singly in the home gardens. For example, the durian tree found in the jungle is tall, struggling to compete for light, whereas a bud-grafted durian tree grown singly in the home garden has a nice conical shape. Trees grown from seeds are different from those obtained by vegetative means. A mango tree grown from seed will develop into a handsome tree with a dome shape crown. Coconut palms both tall and dwarf varieties with green, orange and yellow fruits are available and they look rather attractive swaying in the breeze. One can further exploit the possibility of introducing the lesser known fruit trees especially in the botanical or public gardens so that the people are more aware and exposed to the rich natural resources we are endowed with in this country.

Sukun, Breadfruit, Breadnut
Artocarpus altilis
MORACEAE

The breadfruit is a native of Polynesia and is introduced to many other tropical countries. It grows to a height of 15 metres but is generally less than ten metres. Breadfruit produces huge, dissected, dark, green leaves with very clear venation. The tree produces beautiful, round, green fruits of 10–30 cm diameter.

Nangka, Jackfruit
Artocarpus heterophyllus
MORACEAE

Nangka or jackfruit comes originally from India but is now well-distributed in the tropics. It is a shapely tree, rounded with thick canopy of dark, green, shiny leaves, can grow up to a height of 20 metres. Normally, in the garden it grows to less than ten metres. Jackfruit is a popular tree for the orchard or even as a tree in the home garden, as it provides shade and produces one of the largest fruits of all cultivated fruits. Each fruit weighs up to 20 kilos and measures 30–90 cm by 25–50 cm. The fruits are produced from the main trunk or branches, when ripe it has a very strong smell. Jackfruit is propagated from both seeds and buddings.

Rambai

Baccaurea motleyana

EUPHORBIACEAE

Rambai is a native to Malaysia and Indonesia, grown mainly in villages. The tree is densely leafy and heavy-looking, reaching up to 20 metres.

The crown is rounded and can be used in landscaping. The fruits hang from the branches in chains, each fruit measuring two to four cm, and the chain about half a metre. Fruiting is seasonal, coinciding with the main fruits such as the durian and mangosteen.

Brazilnut
Bertholettia excelsa
LECYTHIDACEAE

Brazilnut is a native of the Amazon forest in South America. Locally it is seldom grown, except in agricultural stations and some rural areas. The tree is very tall, growing as tall as 30 metres with a small crown. At the immature stage the tree is more conical in shape. The leaves are dark green, large and simple, turning to brownish red at senescence. Long panicles of flowers are produced, the flowers are about 2.5 cm wide. The fruits are attached to a thick stalk and are very hard and dark brown in colour. Each

fruit may contain 10–15 nuts which are closely packed. This species is not suitable for planting in the garden as the heavy nuts may fall on people. It is planted from seeds.

Limau Kesturi, Musklime
Citrus microcarpa
RUTACEAE

This is a common plant in the home garden either as a potted plant or planted in the garden as an ornamental or fruit tree. The tree grows to about three to four metres tall. Fruits are produced all year round, they are round, greenish to orangy when ripe. It is easily propagated by marcotting as well as from seeds.

Buah Mentega, Butterfruit
Diospyros discolor
EBENACEAE

Butterfruit is not commonly grown locally but is introduced from the Philippines. Growing to a height of ten metres, it is a small spreading tree with drooping branches. The leaves are smooth but covered with soft fine hairs. Leaves are dark green on the surface but the underside is copper colour because of the hairs which turn to a dull colour at maturity. Flowers are produced in small clusters, they are creamy in colour and slightly scented. The fruits are attractive, rounded, of 5–7.5 cm in diameter, colour varies from pink to reddish brown. It is covered with short silky hairs. This species is a suitable tree for the garden; they are grown from seeds.

Durian
Durio zibethinus
BOMBACEAE

Durian is regarded as the king of fruits in Malaysia and is cultivated in Asia. It is found growing wild in the jungle. Nowadays, it is well-domesticated and grown even in suburban gardens. The tree grows to a height of 40 metres in their wild state. The vegetatively propagated plants are about ten metres high, and has a conical shape with a broad base. The foliage is characterized by the typical bronzy-green, small leaves. In the wild state it has a tall, straight trunk topped by horizontal branches. Fruiting is seasonal, and the thorny fruits are characteristics of this species. Durian trees are generally raised from seeds and buddings.

Jambu Air, Water Apple
Eugenia aquea
MYRTACEAE

Water apple is a native of India, but now widely grown in Malaysia. In cultivation, the tree grows to five or eight metres high. The tree is rounded in shape with fairly large, simple leaves giving a thick canopy. The flowers are very attractive and slightly scented. They are yellow, white or pink depending on varieties. The fruits are also very decorative, white pink to dark red in colour. Water apple can be grown as an ornamental and they are raised from seeds or marcots.

Jambu Bol, Malay Apple
Eugenia malaccensis
MYRTACEAE

This is a distinctive and easily recognized tree because of the very large leaves which are opposite in arrangement. The tree will reach 18 metres eventually and develops an oblong and cylindrical crown. The leaves are simple, 20–36 cm long and 7.5–18 cm wide, slightly drooping, and with a very short stalk of about 1.3 cm long. The deep pink flowers are borne on the leafless portion of the branches and are followed by large fruits 5–7.5 cm long which are oblong and pear-shaped and show a range of colours from white through pink, red and purple. Propagation by seeds.

Manggis, Mangosteen
Garcinia mangostana
CLUSIACEAE (GUTTIFERAE)

Mangosteen is a native of Malaysia grown mainly in villages in rural areas. It is a very slow growing tree reaching to heights of around 13 metres, and takes about 15 years to produce fruits. It is a beautiful tree to have in the garden. The fruits are round and slightly flattened at each end. Each fruit has a smooth, thick, firm rind which is pale green at first and ripening to rich purple or red purple in colour. The fruiting is also seasonal usually following that of the durian. It is propagated by seeds.

Sapucaianut
Lecythis ollaria
LECYTHIDACEAE

This species is less well known than the brazilnut. It is also introduced from South America. The nuts are not grown commercially but are collected from the forest. It is a handsome tree when planted in the garden, producing a large spreading crown. It is much branched and grows to a height of 13 metres. The tree shows signs of wintering at certain times of the year. The fruits are very large, hard and heavy. This species is very slow growing and is grown from seeds.

Mangga, Mango
Mangifera indica
ANACARDIACEAE

Mango is a popular fruit widely distributed all over the tropical areas, has been growing over 4,000 years in India. There are many varieties. The height and shape of trees vary from three to 30 metres. The trees are shapely, some are conical and others rounded; the foliage are dark green and new flushes are colourful, from pinkish to red. As such they are beautiful trees for the garden. The fruits themselves are beautiful and plentiful varying in shapes, colour and sizes. The common varieties are very free flowering and fruiting. Mangoes are also propagated by seeds or budding. Many varieties are polyembryonic, that is they produce a few seedlings from a single seed.

119

Rambutan
Nephelium lappaceum
SAPINDACEAE

Rambutan is a very common fruit grown both in the rural areas as well as suburban homes. It has been cultivated all over Asia, mainly South-East Asia. It is a bushy and wide crowned tree, growing up to 20 metres in height. The vegetatively budgrafted trees are much shorter usually from five to ten metres. This being so, rambutan trees are commonly found in home gardens. Besides being a nice tree by itself, its

fruits are also very attractive, the colour ranges from green yellow to dark red. Rambutan trees are propagated from seeds and budgrafting and start to yield fruits seasonally in one to two years from planting.

Avocado Pear

Persea americana
LAURACEAE

An evergreen tree of up to 20 metres high. Budded trees are normally shorter. This tree with shallow root system is sensitive to poor drainage and cannot stand waterlogging. The leaves are spirally arranged and the flowers are borne at the ends of branches. Flowers are small, 1.3 cm in diameter, fragrant and yellowish in colour. Fruit is large, fleshy and pear-shaped, 7–20 cm long and yellowish green to maroon and purple in colour. Avocados grown from seeds begin bearing at five to six years. Propagation by budding or grafting is the general practice.

Kedondong, Great Hog Plum
Spondias cytherea
ANACARDIACEAE

Kedondong belongs to the same family as the cashewnuts and mangoes. It is introduced from the Pacific but are now grown commonly in the rural areas, at times in the suburban gardens. This species is a fast grower, reaching heights of 10–20 metres. The stem is of light grey colour with dark green, pinnate leaves. It fruits all year round, producing greenish, oblong fruits in bunches. The plant is propagated from seeds.

Asam Jawa, Tamarind
Tamarindus indicus
LEGUMINOSAE

A fine, large tree with a dense, oval crown which will reach 24 metres and is deciduous or almost so. The bark is greyish brown in colour and fissured. After leaf-fall, the new, pale green, young leaves give the tree a light and airy appearance. The leaves are pinnate with small opposite leaflets and when very young can be eaten as these have a sharp, clean flavour. The flowers of tamarind are small, yellow and inconspicuous, but are followed by long, thick pods which contain several seeds surrounded by a juicy pulp. Propagated from seed.

Forest and Plantation Trees

The tropical humid forest in this country top the world list of the greatest number of species and equally famous are our rubber and oil palm. But most Malaysians fail to appreciate this rich, natural resources. Men are destroying the forests by inconsiderate logging and if no control is exerted the forest species may be lost forever. This can be prevented by reforestation and selective logging in existing forests. These resources have to be conserved by establishing seed gardens, arboretum and constantly replanting species that have been removed.

There are many trees in the forests which can be used for beautification purposes in our landscaping programmes. One has to be selective. Some of them are too tall or large and may not be able to tolerate conditions in the concrete jungle. A number of species, however, will do well when they have the necessary conditions.

Equally true species of crop plants can also be made use of as trees for our landscape. An example of this is the oil palm which makes a beautiful avenue. Individual palm also stands out in the compound of a bungalow. The fruits of oil palms, coconut palms and sea apple are colourful and edible. Coffee bushes with their green, red and black berries can be an attractive shrub in the garden.

Many of the forest timber species are suitable for landscaping purposes especially in large gardens and avenues. The main drawback is that they are slow growing. Examples are the jelutong and teak. There are others which are fast growing like the Pinus species and few other smaller, wild trees and shrubs found in our local forests. Many of these trees are beautiful and have yet to be discovered or exploited. They have to be found soon and conserved before they vanish by indiscriminate and destructive logging.

Kapuk, White Silk-Cotton Tree

Ceiba pentandra

BOMBACEAE

The kapok tree is cultivated in tropical Asia and Africa and is a common village tree in Malaysia. A deciduous tree, it reaches 27 metres in height. The trunk is generally wide and stout near the ground with more or less pronounced buttresses, much narrower and neatly cylindric upwards with regular tiers of horizontal branches, giving a narrow, open, thin, pagoda crown. The side branches are also stiffly horizontal, a few upright. The bark is light grey and studded with short conical spines when young. Leaves crowd at the ends of the twigs, leaflets curved back, drooping and glaucous beneath. Normally it sheds its leaves and then flowers and fruits in the dry season. The fruits are attractive at maturity, exposing the fluffy cotton floss. Easily propagated by sticking branches into the ground or from seeds.

Kayu Manis, Indian Cinnamon Tree

Cinnamomum zeylanicum
LAURACEAE

Cinnamon tree is common in the wild conditions of South West India and Sri Lanka, widely cultivated through the East and occasionally planted in gardens and villages in Malaysia. It is an evergreen tree, 8–17 metres high in the wild state. Its bark and leaves are strongly aromatic, the leaves are stiff evergreen. They are reddish when young, turning dark green above with paler veins and pale glaucous beneath. The small flowers are prominent when the tree is in full bloom. Grown solitary and as an avenue tree. They are propagated by seeds.

Angkut-angkut
Commersonea bartramnia
STERCULIACEAE

This is a small, wild tree which will grow to ten metres in height with an open crown and branches arranged horizontally, giving a layered appearance. Large numbers of flowers and fruits are produced along the upper surface of each branch. The flowers are small with white petals and is followed by small, round, hairy fruits. The tree is evergreen and flowers throughout the year. It can be planted singly or in a mixed group.

Kelapa, Coconut
Cocos nucifera
PALMAE

Coconut palms are very common along the coastal areas in the tropics. In almost every village coconut palms are planted, ranging from single palm to plantations. Varieties with different coloured fruits (green, yellow, pinkish red and brownish) are available and their habit varies from dwarf (four metres) to tall (25 metres). The palm grows slowly in the initial stage and bears fruits when three to 12 years old depending on the variety. Coconut palms have a place in landscaping. Even a single palm can be attractive and useful in the compound of a house. They can be planted in groups of various heights or in rows as avenues. Coconut palms are propagated from seeds

Jelutong
Dyera costulata
APOCYNACEAE

Jelutong is a magnificent, tall tree. Originated from Sumatra and the Peninsular Malaysia. It possesses an unbuttressed, columnar trunk, reaching a height of over 60 metres. The crown is dense, forming a shallow dome. Grown as a solitary individual or planted as an avenue, it is deciduous and sheds its leaves once a year. The tree is bare for only a few days before new leaf flush comes on, making the crown bronze pink for another few days. Flowers are small, developing with the new leaves. The young trees often have twisted trunks but straighten up later. They are grown from seeds.

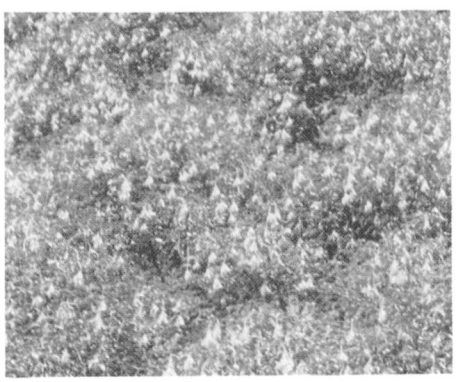

Kapur, Borneo Camphor Tree
Dryobalanops aromatica
DIPTEROCARPACEAE

It is one of the tallest timber trees in the Indo-Malayan tropics, frequently attaining more than 60 metres in height. A large tree with light fawn, brown bark and large, scaly flakes. The crown is very finely leaved and elegant. The leaves are five to ten cm long and pointed. The flowers are white, fragrant and two cm wide. General flowering occurs every three to four years. In full bloom the trees are very attractive. They are propagated from seeds.

Pokok Kelapa Sawit, Oil Palm
Elaeis guineensis
PALMAE

Oil palm originally came from the tropical rain forest region of West Africa. An unbranched palm of 20–30 metres in height, it may live up to 200 years. A trunk is not formed until the seedling is three years old when the apex has reached its full diameter in the form of an inverted cone. Leaf bases which adhere to the stem for 12 years give the palm a rough stemmed appearance. The leaf bases then fall away except for a few near the crown giving the palm a smooth stem with scars of leaf bases and encircling sheaths. Mature leaf measures up to 7.5 metres long with 250–300 linear leaflets. Flowering inflorescences are produced in the axil of leaf. Male inflorescences have fingerlike spineless cylindrical spikes whereas female inflorescences are thick and fleshy in the axils of spiny bract and a terminal spine. The fruit bunch is attractive, colour ranging from red to almost black. It is grown as a solitary palm or as an avenue tree. Propagation from seeds and tissue culture.

Eucalyptus deglupta
MYRTACEAE

This eucalyptus originates from New Guinea and was introduced into the West Indies. It tolerates a wide range of climatic and soil conditions. It is not commonly grown in the very wet tropics at low altitudes. Eucalyptus often grows to 60–70 metres and 1.5 metres in diameter. This tree has a beautiful trunk of grey, green and pinkish colour and the bark peels off revealing the smooth stem. Propagation is from seeds.

Pokok Getah, Para Rubber
Hevea brasiliensis
EUPHORBIACEAE

Rubber or hevea grows wild in the tropical rain forests of South America. But under cultivation, it grows well on moist, well-drained, loamy soils. It grows quickly, rarely exceeding 25 metres in height in plantations; but in the wild, the trees are over 40 metres. Individual trees in home garden grow to different shapes. Leaves are spirally arranged, trifoliate, glabrous. Young leaves are purple bronze, becoming green on hardening. In dry weather, the leaves turn orange brown, red or yellow before falling and this phase is termed 'wintering'. The flowers are borne in many flowered panicles on basal part of a new flush and they are scented. Propagated by seeds and budding.

Telinga Gajah, Giant Mahang
Macaranga gigantea
EUPHORBIACEAE

A medium sized tree up to 20 metres high with thick twigs carrying large leaves. The leaves are 20 cm to 80 cm long and broad with three to five large lobes, and very large petioles. It is a common wild tree and should be used for its large leaves which are very decorative. Seedlings develop the largest leaves. In matured plants the leaves are smaller, but they still provide a welcome change from the numerous tree species with much smaller leaves. This species is best grown in mixed groups so that its large leaves provide sufficient contrast with those of the other species.

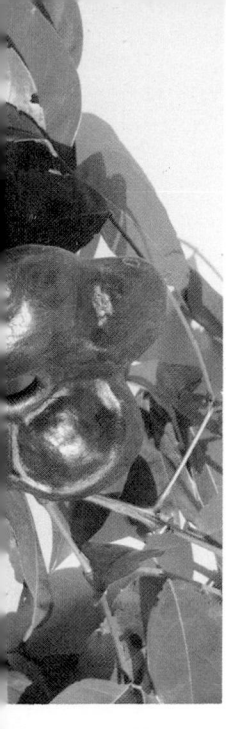

Jering
Pithecellobium jiringa
LEGUMINOSAE

Jering is commonly grown in Malaysia, in secondary jungles and in villages. It is medium size, growing up to 25 metres high with large, rounded crown; bark is light pinkish brown and smooth. Young leaves are rich purple providing a colourful crown. Leaves are glabrous and the flowers are in small heads of three to six flowers and are arranged in panicles 10–22 cm long in the older leaf axils or on the twigs behind the leaves. Pods are massive, five cm wide, strongly lobed, leathery, dull purplish brown in colour and coiled in two circles in opposite directions. Grown from seeds.

Meranti Pipit

Shorea assamica

DIPTEROCARPACEAE

Meranti pipit is often found in lowlying land near streams. It is a large tree with more than three metres girth and has pink inner bark. This tree has large, sharp buttresses, shallowly and irregularly fissured. The young parts of the twigs are reddish. The flowers are two cm at its broadest with white petals and tinged pink inside. Propagation from seeds.

Kayu Jati, Teak
Tectona grandis
VERBENACEAE

Teak is well-known as a timber species, mainly found in South-East Asia including Malaysia. It is a fine, handsome tree with large leaves doing well in drier climate of the tropics but not in dense tropical rain forest. Teak is not found readily in home gardens except in botanical gardens and arboretums. It grows well in good soil to a height of 15 metres. Bears flowers and fruits. Seeds are used for propagation.

Palms and Bamboos

Generally speaking, palms are always formal in appearance. They can be used in combination with other trees but then the palm crown needs to be visible between the other tree crowns or, at a later stage, should be held above them to get a truly tropical effect. As palms are relatively slow growing, this effect would take several years to achieve.

Although many palms produce a single stem, there are a number of species in which each plant has several stems and these are usually more useful for formal planting. The larger single stemmed palms can be planted singly or in avenues but are not so attractive in small groups except when they are young and before the stem has developed to any great length. The flowers of the palms are, on the whole, inconspicuous except in species that have a large inflorescence. When many of the flowers open simultaneously the inflorescence can be very attractive for a short time. Many palms produce large quantities of fruits and in a number of species these become bright red when ripe so that the plants are very handsome in appearance. The inflorescences may be held amongst the leaves or below the leaves on the bare stem.

Palms are of two kinds, those with fan leaves and those with feather leaves. In the former, the leaves are round and in most cases have a lobed margin or are divided into several leaflets all arising from one point at the top of the leaf stalk. In the latter the leaves are elongated and the blade is dissected into many leaflets all held on a rachis.

Palm leaves are held stiffly on the stem and as they age they tend to hang downwards. In the fan palms this results in the familiar round crown, but in the feather palms, the leaves sometimes become brown and hang closely around the stem. This can be unsightly but the dead leaves are easily removed. In some palms the base of the leaf stalk remains on the stem and often small epiphytic ferns will grow between them. This gives a settled and natural look to the palm and the ferns cause no damage.

Coconut palms, although decorative are perhaps not suitable for planting in public areas because of the danger of falling fruits. But this can be avoided by regular harvesting.

Pinang, Betel Nut Palm
Areca catechu
PALMAE

A slender stemmed palm of up to 20 metres in height with a smooth, grey trunk marked with circular leaf scars. The young portions of the stem are green. The pinnate leaves have many dark green, stiff leaflets and are arched so that the tips tend to point downwards. The inflorescences develop just below the leaves and the flowers have a strong, sweet smell. The fruits are bright orange when ripe. This palm can be planted singly, in groups or in mixed planting; but it has no sufficient stature to be used for avenue planting.

Hedge Bamboo

Bambusa nana (= glaucescens)
GRAMINEAE

The stems will reach up to four metres in height and if so allowed, will have unrestricted growth. When used as a hedge it must be carefully trimmed and will then produce many side branches carrying leaves from each node in the stem. Leaves are short, and narrow with parallel sides. Propagated by division.

Buddha's Belly Bamboo
Bambusa ventricosa
GRAMINEAE

This species will grow to 15 or 20 metres in height when planted directly in the ground, but if grown in large pots or in poor soil the stems are much shorter (two to three metres high) and the internodes are swollen, hence the common name of the plant.

Common Bamboo
Bambusa vulgaris
GRAMINEAE

A plant which forms large, open clumps and which needs to be controlled to prevent it spreading over too large an area. The species will reach 20 metres or more in height and there are a number of varieties in which the leaves and stems are variously striped with yellow. The leaves are large and broad, up to 25 cm in length. Fallen leaves form a thick mat around the base of the stems and prevent the growth of other plants. Continuous leaf-fall is a problem as frequent sweeping is necessary.

Lontar, Sea Apple, Palmyra Palm
Borassus flabellifera
PALMAE

The sea apple is of Asiatic origin, but is commonly found in the northern part of Peninsular Malaysia. It is fairly tall palm growing up to 10–20 metres. Every part of the palm is useful and it produces a beautiful crown of large palmate leaves. The fruits are borne in bunches like coconuts but are much smaller, rounded and purplish green in colour. The fruit measures about 10–12.5 cm in diameter and is slightly flattened at both ends. Sea apple is propagated by seeds.

Rabuk, Fish-tail Palm
Caryota mitis
PALMAE

A species which will reach four to five metres in height and can form a clump with a few tall stems and many suckers. It is unusual as it has bipinnate leaves with leaflets that are widest at the apex and are shaped like a fish tail. The inflorescences develop from the top of the stem downwards. In later stages the whole stem dies. The fruits are produced in large, pendulous clusters. This is a fine species for single planting or in mixed groups.

Chrysalidocarpus lutescens
PALMAE

An introduced palm commonly planted for decorative purposes. It can be grown in pots or directly in the ground and produces a large number of sucker shoots so that eventually the plant forms a dense clump. Older shoots elongate and arch slightly outwards from the centre of the clump. The leaves are pinnate and are slightly curved downwards. They have numerous narrow light green leaflets. The species can be used effectively in a formal planting arrangement and the number of sucker shoots can be reduced to keep the plant tidy in appearance. It can be propagated easily from suckers especially if these have some roots and will grow up to three metres in height.

Talipot Palm
Corypha umbracaulifera
PALMAE

This is a very large palm with enormous leaves and is introduced to this country. It has a single massive trunk bearing a crown of fan leaves each of which may be 2.5 metres in length. The basal part of the lamina is entire but the margin is cut deeply into a number of broad leaflets. The leaves are light green and often are yellowish in appearance. This species only flowers after many years of growth and the flowers develop a very large inflorescence of up to seven metres in length. After flowering and fruiting, the whole plant dies but many hundreds of seeds are produced. The large, stiff leaves give these plants an appearance of great strength and they are probably best planted near very large buildings or in parks where they can be viewed from a distance.

Cycas

CYCADACEAE

Two species are commonly grown and may be used as potted plants or grown directly in the ground. Both species are very formal in appearance with a very short trunk carrying a crown made up of one to three rows of long, dark green, pinnate leaves. The leaflets are long and narrow and are very leathery in texture. Growth is very slow and once planted these species should be left undisturbed. Very old plants sometimes develop branches but this only occurs after many years and such plants may reach three metres in height. Young plants remain between one and 1.5 metres for a very long time.

Pinang Raja, Sealing Wax Palm

Cyrtostachys lakka

PALMAE

A palm with pinnate leaves and a number of stems forming a small clump. Many sucker shoots develop and several tall stems arise from among them. The leaves and leaflets are stiff in character and are usually directed obliquely upwards. The stem may reach 12-13 metres in height and the leaves are up to two metres long. The young leaf sheaths are bright scarlet but this coloration does not develop until the palms are several years old. The plant may be grown in pots for a long time as their growth is slow.

Kelapa Sawit, Oil Palm
Elaeis guineensis
PALMAE

The oil palm can be used in planting schemes and may be grown as single specimen plant or in groups or avenues. When used for avenue planting it should be placed at least three metres away from the road or pathside otherwise the large leaves will block the road while the palms are young. The species will reach 30 metres in height after many years. It has pinnate leaves up to seven metres long with large dark green leaflets and the flowers and fruits are produced near the base of the leaf stalk. As the stem becomes taller and the older leaves fall many small epiphytes, especially ferns, grow amongst the leaf bases on the stem. Some orchids and begonias can be encouraged to grow there also.

Palas
Licuala grandis
PALMAE

A short palm with fan leaves and which will eventually grow to two metres in height. The leaf blade is entire, dark green and rounded with a deeply toothed margin and may be up to 60 cm long and 50 cm broad. The plants may be grown in pots but will remain small and are probably best planted directly in the ground. It is useful for mixed planting as the large leaves make a useful contrast in size with the many plants which have small and medium sized leaves.

Licuala spinosus
PALMAE

In this species the plant produces a number of stems and eventually forms a dense clump. It can reach seven metres in height and has long leaves with a number of wedge-shaped leaflets. Each leaf can be 45–60 cm long and the leaflets are up to eight cm broad. Flowers are produced on sprays up to three metres in length and eventually are replaced by attractive orange fruits. The plant can be grown singly or in a large mixed planting scheme, but in the latter case the form of the leaves may be concealed by the neighbouring plants.

Chinese Fan Palm
Livistona chinensis
PALMAE

A tall palm from eight to ten metres in height with fan-shaped leaves. The central part of the leaf is entire but the edge is divided into a number of long, narrow leaflets with drooping tips making the plant easily recognizable. When young the plant is hemispherical and only loses this shape after several years when the stem has elongated. This palm can be grown singly, in groups, or as an avenue plant and looks well near tall buildings and in large open courtyards. The crown of leaves in old plants is almost spherical in shape.

Nibung
Oncosperma tigillarium
PALMAE

A tall species forming large clumps and found wild in coastal areas. The stems and leaf stalks are covered with long, strong spines. The species should not be planted close to public pathways. However, a large clump is elegant in appearance because of the slender stems and drooping leaflets of the leaves. Because the plant becomes very tall it is most suitable for growing near tall buildings. The stems may reach 20 metres or more in length. The leaves are pinnate with many narrow leaflets and are dull green in colour. The stems and the leaf sheaths bear long, black spines. The shape and size of this plant makes it excellent for landscape design work and it is probably best planted singly in positions where it can be viewed from some distance.

Ptychoraphis augusta
PALMAE

An introduced palm with a single stem and a crown of pinnate leaves having narrow drooping leaflets. The stem shows ring-shaped leaf scars. Inflorescences develop below the leaves. The palm can be planted singly or in groups or in mixed planting.

Ptychosperma macarthurii
PALMAE

A species forming a small clump with stems up to five metres high and with pinnate leaves. The leaflets are broad and the flowers are produced on inflorescences below the leaves. This species can be grown in large pots but is also suitable for group planting and in an avenue. The younger parts of the stems remain smooth and dark green for a long time and are marked by ring-shaped leaf scars.

Traveller's Palm
Ravenala madagascariensis
STRELITZIACEAE

This is not a palm at all nor member of the banana family. It has a stout trunk producing leaves in two rows so that a fan shape is produced. The plants often produce suckers from the base and these can be removed for propagation or can be allowed to remain so that the plant forms a large clump. It has large, broad, oblong leaves with long petioles which are developed close together so that when viewed from the end of the 'fan' the plant is only the width of the stem, but from the side the diameter of the crown which is flat, may be four to six metres. It does not usually flower in the lowlands but is reported to grow naturally at 1,200 metres and would probably flower in highland areas of the country. It is an excellent plant for avenue planting or for single planting and is very dramatic in appearance. If the planting position is too windy the leaves quickly become very ragged although this is not at all unsightly.

Rhapis excelsa
PALMAE

A fan palm often grown in pots for indoor decorating. It makes a dense clump and each leaf may have up to 11 leaflets. The stems are slender and the plant can reach three metres in height. When planted in the ground it makes a very dense, bushy plant needing little attention and it retains its leaves down to ground level. In pots very short suckers give rise to the stems but in the ground some suckers may extend to one metre or more in length. This species can be used for formal planting or in a mixed group and always retains a tidy appearance.

Royal Palm
Roystonea regia
PALMAE

A tall palm with a large crown of pinnate leaves. The plants will reach 20 metres or more in height and the trunk is smooth with a pale grey surface. The stem becomes thicker below the crown but if water or nutrients are restricted thickening does not occur. The leaves are very large, up to 3.5 metres long with the leaflets arranged in four rows so that the palm's general appearance is cylindrical. The large inflorescences are produced below the leaves and eventually carry many rounded, dark red or purple fruits, while R. oleracea fruits are oblong. This palm is most suitable for avenue planting or for single planting.

Veitchia merrilli
PALMAE

A commonly grown single stemmed palm of up to ten metres in height. The leaves are pinnate, dark green with broad leaflets and are arched. Inflorescences are produced below the leaves on the stem and eventually clusters of bright red fruits which are very attractive develop. The species can be grown singly or as an avenue plant.

Propagation, Planting and Maintenance

PROPAGATION

Shrubs and trees are commonly propagated or reproduced sexually by seeds or vegetatively by cuttings of various types, marcotting and grafting. The method of propagation depends on the type of species. Some can only reproduce by seeds and others which do not flower produce vegetatively. Many can be propagated both by seed and vegetative means. There are advantages and disadvantages in both methods of propagation. With seeds one can get more variation in the end product; by vegetative means all the progenies from the same mother plant will be identical. Vegetative propagation also offers rapid reproduction of a large number of plants which will come to maturity much earlier. For example, a woody stem cutting of angsana will produce new shoots once the roots grow. A tree of two metres high is established within months.

Whereas from a seed it may take a year or two before it reaches that height. When planting, one must therefore be aware of the method of propagation of the species, what are the facilities available and the number of plants required.

Seeds

Tree seeds are not normally available in the market as with flower and vegetable seeds. They are also seasonal in nature, producing once or twice a year. Some exceptions may flower and set seeds all year round. Tree seeds are usually bigger than flower and vegetable seeds hence there is less problem in handling and sowing. Seeds are often sown in a seed box or in individual polythene bag. When they reach 10–15 cm, they can be transplanted into individual bags and kept under shade in a nursery (Figure 1A). Seedlings have to be looked after by proper watering and regular fertilization. Once they reach a height of a metre they can be transplanted into a planting hole in the garden, avenue, car parks and parks.

Vegetative propagation

There are various forms of vegetative propagation such as grafting, marcotting and cuttings. Both grafting and marcotting are often used for fruits, for trees and shrubs different types of cuttings are used. They are hardwood cuttings and softwood cuttings. The hardwood cuttings are taken from the mature twigs or branches that are hardened while the softwood or young cuttings arise from the tips of branches and are often still green.

In making a cutting, use a sharp knife or secateur to get a clean cut. Most of the leaves are removed from the cuttings to prevent loss of water. The cut ends are usually dipped in a rooting mixture of hormones to stimulate rooting. Cuttings are often

Figure 1A

Figure 1B

rooted in moist sand beds kept moist by regular sprinkling of water (Figure 1B). Within days or weeks roots and new shoots or buds will appear indicating success. Once they have rooted and leaves are appearing they can be hardened by exposing them to full sunlight for a couple of days. The cuttings can then be transplanted to individual bags.

Hardwood cuttings of two to five cm diameter and length of 1.5 to two metres can also be used for some tree species like angsana. Straight lengths of angsana cuttings can be planted directly into a planting hole as some of these species root readily and are quite hardy. Thus a sizeable tree is produced in a short period of time.

PLANTING

Not many people know how to plant a tree correctly. The common questions are how, when and where to plant. Unlike fruits, vegetables and other ornamental plants, trees are often planted in odd places like car parks and along footpaths which are not very suitable for plant growth as the top surface is often tarred or covered with concrete slabs so that the trees often suffer from inadequate aeration and water. Special care is required in planting a tree under such a condition.

In planting a tree or shrub under any situation, it is desirable to prepare a planting hole of a metre square and a metre deep. The soil should be well cultivated and organic manure incorporated into the soil and well mixed. In the planting hole excavate or remove soil in the middle to fit the new seedling or cutting in a polythene bag (Figure 2). A seedling or a newly marcotted plant in a plastic bag is first split open and placed carefully in the centre of the planting hole, then the

hole is filled with soil which is pressed firmly around the newly planted tree. If the stem is weak, a stake is necessary. Tie the stem to the stake for support and also to train the plant for upright growth. After planting, water the plant sufficiently well and place some dead leaves around the base of the plant to prevent moisture loss and weed growth.

In public gardens, parks and hotels where an 'instant' garden is often necessary to attract people, 'instant' trees of over three metres tall can be planted. Such large seedlings or trees are specially planted for this purpose. They are planted in large pots or boxes so that they can be transported easily from the nursery to the place of planting. In this case, a planting hole is also necessary and less soil is required in the planting hole as compared to the small polythene bags. These big pots or boxes have to be first removed and the tree with the whole ball of earth is to be carefully lowered into the planting hole. The soil around is then compacted and dead leaves placed around the base and the tree is then watered.

Bigger trees growing in the nursery bed or in another part of the garden can also be transplanted, in this case it is a more specialized type of job requiring some heavy expensive equipment. A tree of four metres high has to be transplanted. This has to be done in stages by making a cut at a time, at weekly intervals on the four

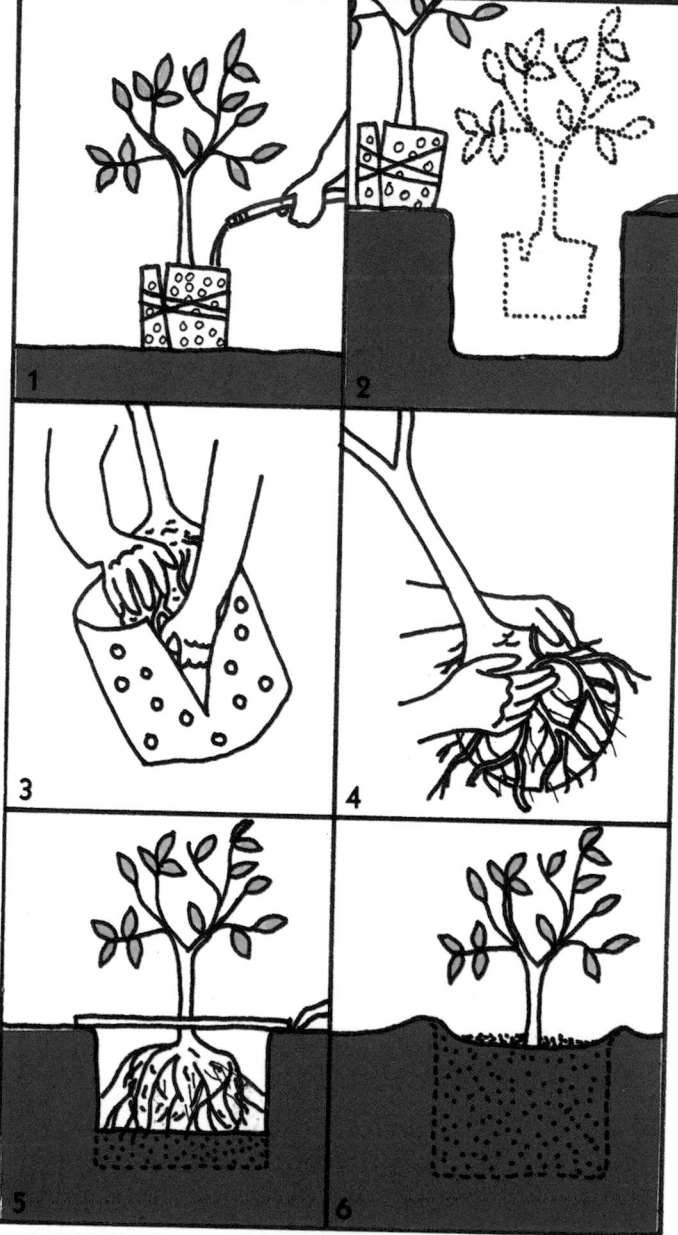

Figure 2

sides of the tree. The cut may be as deep as a metre (Figure 3). After about four weeks, the whole tree is dug up with the huge shovel of a front end loader tractor. The ball of earth

The tree is then transported to the transplanting site where a big hole of 1.5 metre square is ready to receive the tree. The tree is carefully lowered into the hole. More soil is added; and make sure that the newly transplanted tree is firmly in the hole by compacting the soil around the stem and if need be, a temporary stake is put in (Figure 5).

Figure 3

with the whole root system is bagged with gunny sack or hessian cloth so that on transporting the earth the whole root system is intact (Figure 4).

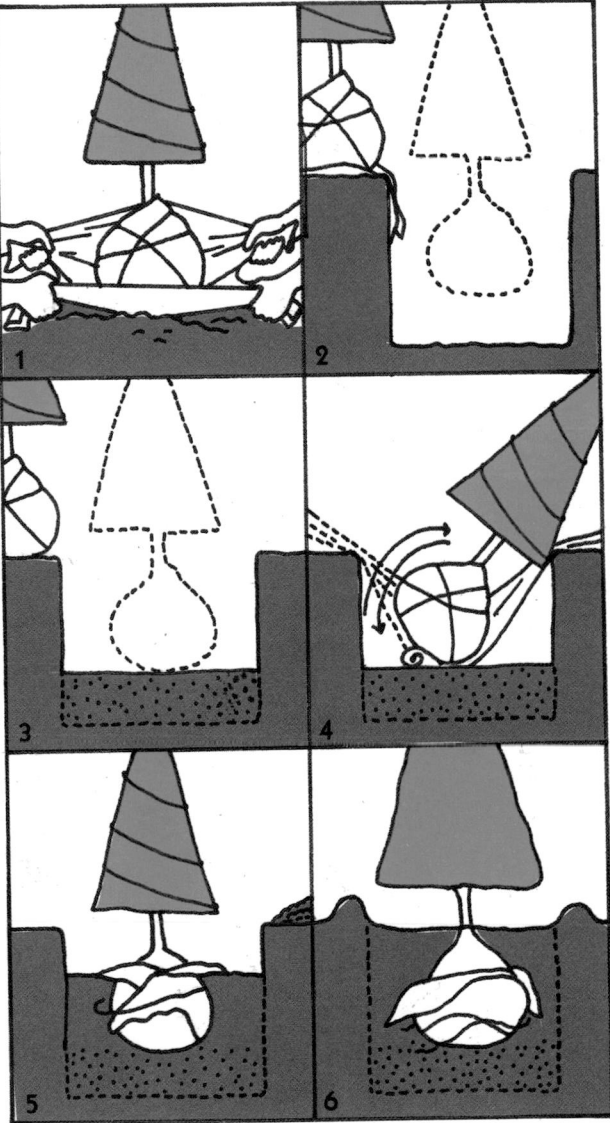

Figure 5

Figure 4

In case of planting along footpaths, pavements or car park, make sure that the tree hole has sufficient space for aeration and water. There should be an area around the main trunk of the tree free of paving. Kerbs with adequate openings for excess water to run off and strong enough to guard the trees from being hit by vehicles are required (Figure 6). The unpaved area around the main trunk can either be turfed, ground covers can be grown, or an organic mulch of dead leaves and bark be provided (Figure 7).

MAINTENANCE

Many shrubs and trees are planted in areas with adverse conditions for growth such as in the centre of cities, footpaths and pavements. These are the plants that need more special attention than trees planted in a garden. A tree needs regular watering, fertilizing, pruning and protecting from all types of pests and diseases.

A newly planted tree has to be given special care especially in a concrete jungle where it is hotter and drier than in the garden or natural forest. It has to be watered daily with care not just with a splatter of water here and there but with sufficient water to soak through the soil. Once it is firmly established, regular watering is not necessary. A tree requires food, therefore fertilizer has to be provided twice or three times a year. The fertilizer has to be well integrated with the soil by raking the soil under the canopy of the tree. Weeds around

Figure 6

Figure 7

the tree have to be removed. Very often, a beautiful tree or shrub is spoilt by the unsightly weeds around.

A tree has to be trained and groomed to look its best. Shapes can be imposed on the tree. For example, the bougainvillea can be an upright plant or a creeper depending on how it is trained initially. If an upright tree is required the young plant has to be staked and all side shoots removed leaving a single, main stem. Most trees will take on its natural shape if left untouched, like the cone shape of the junipers and the rounded crown of the milletia tree. However, man can shape the trees to his liking, an art called topiary, by which trees can be shaped to look like animals. In addition to the shaping of trees, regular pruning is necessary for those flowering and fruiting trees. To encourage free fruiting and flowering, the branches have to be pruned to induce new growth of shoots, flowers and subsequently fruits. Shrubs and trees like other crop plants or ornamentals are susceptible to attack by pests and diseases, but they are comparatively more resistant. The principles and methods of control are similar to those for fruit trees if the causal organisms are the same. The common pesticides can be used with the same instructions and precautions as for fruit trees.

Index

COMMON NAME

A

African Tulip Tree	96
Akasia Kuning	16
Angkut-angkut	130
Angsana	90
Asam Jawa	125
Avocado Pear	123

B

Baru-baru	59
Batai	79
Bedara	180
Beremban Bukit	176
Betel Nut Palm	144
Borneo Camphor Tree	134
Bottle-brush Tree	29
Brazilnut	110
Breadfruit	106
Breadnut	106
Broad leafed Mahogany	98
Buah Mentega	113
Buddha's Belly Bamboo	146
Bungur	64, 66
Bur Flower Tree	22
Busuk-busuk	176
Buta-buta	36
Butterfruit	113

C

Cajeput	67
Cempaka Merah	71
Cempaka Putih	178
Cempedak	176
Chinese Date	180
Chinese Fan Palm	156
Coconut	131
Common Bamboo	147
Cucur Atap	25

D

Dedap	47
Durian	114

F

Fish-tail Palm	149
Flame of the Forest	41
Frangipanni	85

G

Gelam	67
Gelam Bukit	177
Gemunggai	178
Geti	179
Giant Mahang	138
Great Hog Plum	124

H

Hedge Bamboo	145
Horse Cassia	33
Horse-radish Tree	178

I

Indian Cinnamon Tree	129
Indian Jujube	180
Indian Laburnum	32
Ironwood Tree	70

J

Jackfruit	108
Jambu Air	115
Jambu Bol	116
Jambu Laut	48
Jambul Merak	61
Japanese Cherry	75
Jati Laut	86
Jelutong	132
Jeneris	72
Jering	139
Johor	33
Juniper	63

K

Kapuk	128
Kapur	134
Kassod Tree	33
Kayu Jati	141
Kayu Manis	37, 129
Kedondong	124
Kelapa	131
Kelapa Sawit	154
Kelempayan	22
Kelumpang	180
Kelumpang Burung	97
Kembang Semangkuk	179
Kemboja	85
Kenanga	31
Ketapang	100
Kotek	33
Kupu Orchid Tree	26

L

Limau Kesturi	111
Lokus	60
Lontar	148

M

Madras Thorn	80
Malabirah Cabbage Tree	49
Malay Apple	116
Mambu	69

Mangga 119
Manggis 117
Mango 119
Mangosteen 117
Margosa Tree 69
Mata Kucing 19
Medang Kelawar 179
Mempari 88
Mempat 39
Mempoyan 179
Mengkudu 74
Meranti Pipit 140
Mexican Lilac 57
Mindi Kecil 178
Musklime 111

N
Nangka 108
Nibung 156
Nim Tree 69
Norfolk Pine 24

O
Oil Palm 154
Orange Tree Hibiscus 177

P
Palas 155
Palmyra Palm 148
Pancut 96
Para Rubber 137
Pelawan 180
Penaga 70
Penaga Laut 30
Perah 45
Persian Lilac 178
Petai 178
Petai Jawa 177
Pinang 144
Pinang Raja 153
Pine 80
Pink Cassia 176
Pokok Getah 137
Pong-pong 36
Potato Tree 95
Pride of Burma 21
Pukul Lima 92
Pulai 20

R
Rabuk 149
Rain Tree 92
Rajah Kayu 32
Rambai 109
Rambutan 121
Randa 56
Rose of India 66
Royal Palm 161
Ru 34

S
Saga 19
Saga Gajah 83
Sapucaianut 118
Screw Pine 77
Sea Almond 100
Sea Apple 48, 148
Sea Hibiscus 59
Sea Teak 86
Sealing Wax Palm 153
Semarak Api 41
Sena 90
Sentang 68
Sepalir 180
Sial Menahun 89
Silky Oak 177
Silver Back 179
Star Apple 176
Sukun 106

T
Taban Putih 76
Talipot Palm 150
Tamarind 125
Tanjung 73
Tapak Kuda 26
Teak 141
Telinga Gajah 138
Tembusu 50
Traveller's Palm 158
Tree Fern 39
Tree of Life 103
Turi 179
Tutuk 177

W
Water Apple 115
Wattle 16
West Indian Locust Tree 60
White Gutta 76
White Silk-Cotton Tree 128
Wild Cinnamon 37
Willow 91, 179

Y
Yellow Flame 79
Yellow Oleander 102
Yellow Saraca 94

BOTANICAL NAME

A
Acacia auriculaeformis 16
Acacia cicinnata 17
Acacia mangium 17
Adenanthera pavonina 19
Albizzia falcata 19
Alstonia augustifolia 20
Amherstia nobilis 21
Anthocephalus cadamba 22
Araucaria bidwillii 23
Araucaria excelsa 24
Areca catechu 144

Artocarpus altilis 106
Artocarpus heterophyllus 108
Artocarpus integer 176

B

Baccaurea motleyana 109
Baeckia frutescens 25
Bambusa nana 145
Bambusa ventricosa 146
Bambusa vulgaris 147
Bauhinia blakeana 26
Bertholettia excelsa 110
Borassus flabellifera 148

C

Callistemon sp. 29
Calophyllum inophyllum 30
Canagium odoratum 31
Caryota mitis 149
Cassia fistula 32
Cassia grandis 33
Cassia nodosa 176
Cassia siamea 33
Casuarina 34
Casuarina equisetifolia 34
Casuarina nobilis 35
Casuarina rumphiana 35
Ceiba pentandra 128
Cerbera manghas 36
Chrysalidocarpus lutescens 150
Chrysophyllum cainito 176
Cinnamomum iners 37
Cinnamomum zeylanicum 129
Citrus microcarpa 111
Cocos nucifera 131
Commersonea bartramnia 130
Corypha umbracaulifera 150
Cratoxylon formosum 39
Cyathea 39
Cycas 152
Cyrtostachys lakka 153

D

Delonix regia 41
Diospyros discolor 113
Dryobalanops aromatica 134
Duabanga sonnerationdes 176
Durio zibethinus 114
Dyera costulata 132

E

Elaeis guineensis 154
Elateriospermum tapos 45
Enterolobium cyclocarpum 45
Erythrina 47
Erythrina orientalis 47
Erythrina var. 47
Erythrina variegata 47
Eucalyptus deglupta 136
Eugenia aquea 115
Eugenia grandis 48
Eugenia malaccensis 116

F

Fagraea crenulata 49
Fagraea fragrans 50
Ficus benjamina 52
Ficus elastica 51
Ficus religiosa 54
Ficus roxburghii 54
Firmiana fulgens 55

G

Garcinia mangostana 117
Gardenia carinata 56
Gliricidia sepium 57
Grevillea robusta 177
Gustavia superba 58

H

Hevea brasiliensis 137
Hibiscus floccosus 177
Hibiscus tiliaceus 59
Hymenaea courboril 60

J

Jacaranda filicifolia 61
Juniperus 63

L

Lagerstroemia floribunda 64
Lagerstroemia speciosa 66
Lecythis ollaria 118
Leptospermum flavescens 177
Leucaena leucocephala 177
Licuala grandis 155
Licuala spinosus 155
Livistona chinensis 156

M

Macaranga gigantea 138
Mangifera indica 119
Melaleuca leucadendron 67
Melia azederach 178
Melia excelsa 68
Melia indica 69
Mesua ferrea 70
Michaelia alba 178
Michaelia champaka 71
Milletia atropurpurea 72
Mimusops elengi 73
Morinda citrifolia 74
Moringa oleifera 178
Muntingia calabura 75

N

Nephelium lappaceum 121

O

Oncosperma tigillarium 156

P

Palaquium obovatum 76
Pandanus 77
Parkia speciosa 178

Peltophorum pterocarpum 79
Persea americana 123
Pinus caribaea 80
Pithecellobium dulce 80
Pithecellobium ellipticum 83
Pithecellobium jiringa 139
Plumeria acuta 85
Plumeria obtusa 85
Plumeria rubra 85
Podocarpus polystachyos 86
Podocarpus rumphii 86
Polyalthia longifolia 87
Pometia pinnata 87
Pongamia pinnata 88
Pternandra echinata 89
Pterocarpus indicus 90
Ptychoraphis augusta 157
Ptychosperma macarthurii 157
Pygeum polystachum 179

R
Ravenala madagascariensis 158
Rhapis excelsa 159
Rhodamnia trimerva 179
Roystonea oleracea 161
Roystonea regia 161

S
Salix sp. 91

Salix tetrasperma 179
Samanea saman 92
Saraca indica 93
Saraca thaipingensis 94
Scaphium affine 179
Sesbania grandiflora 179
Shorea assamica 140
Sindora coriacea 180
Solanum wrightii 95
Spathodea campanulata 96
Spondias cytherea 124
Sterculia foetida 180
Sterculia parviflora 97
Swietenia macrophylla 98

T
Tabebuiea rosea 99
Tamarindus indicus 125
Tectona grandis 141
Terminalia catappa 100
Thevetia peruviana 102
Thuja 103
Tristania sumatrana 180

V
Veitchia merrilli 162

Z
Zizyphus jujuba 180

Appendix
List of Trees without Illustrations

Cempedak
Artocarpus integer
MORACEAE

An evergreen tree of 20 or 25 metres high with a conical crown that later becomes rounded. The simple leaves are ovate with an acute apex and have a thin covering of wiry hairs. The tiny flowers are produced in stout inflorescences and the male and female flowers develop on separate inflorescences on the same tree. The male inflorescences are green and cylindrical and are often produced near the tips of the branches. The female inflorescences are massive and develop on the trunk and main branches. The fruits are up to 35 cm by 15–20 cm broad, often irregular in shape and the whole surface is covered with very short spines. They have a very strong smell. The trees are interesting when planted as the plant has a most unusual appearance when the trunk and main branches are carrying many fruits.

Busuk-busuk, Pink Cassia
Cassia nodosa
LEGUMINOSAE

A native tree that will reach 24 metres in height and is deciduous. It is slightly flat-topped, but the crown often becomes rounded and it has long, pinnate leaves with relatively small leaflets. The pink flowers are produced in dense clusters on the branches behind the leaves. They are followed by long, straight, green pods which become black when ripe and give the tree a distinctive appearance for some time. Propagation by seeds.

Star Apple
Chrysophyllum cainito
SAPOTACEAE

A very beautiful species with a dark green slightly open crown which is oval when young and later spreading. The tree can reach 15 metres in height and has simple alternate leaves which are elliptic with an acute apex, and a very short stalk. They may reach 18 cm in length and 10 cm in width, and the upper surface is a dark glossy green whereas the under-surface is covered with short, shining copper-coloured hairs. The pale, purple flowers are borne in clusters in the leaf axils and are followed by large round fruits 7.5 cm in diameter which become white or purple when ripe and are edible. This is an introduced tree and is especially attractive when the wind blows through the foliage as the silky coppery undersides of the leaves give it a totally different aspect. It is not common and does not fruit very well here. Can be propagated by marcotting.

Beremban Bukit
Duabanga sonnerationdes
LYTHRACEAE

Native to India and Peninsular Malaysia. A very characteristically shaped, evergreen tree with a single, main trunk carrying drooping, lateral branches which develop in whorls with two to four branches in each. The large simple leaves are opposite in arrangement and are pink when young. They can be from 15–30 cm long and five to ten cm wide with a heart-shaped base and a very short petiole. Bark is light brown often with the pinkish tint. Large leaf scars are visible. Flowers are large and are carried on a terminal cluster. Each flower is about 7.5 cm wide and opens in the evening followed by a fruit with the prominent starlike calyx at the apex. Propagation by seeds. The drooping appearance would be useful when planted either as a specimen or in a group. Could be used near buildings or in parks in most soils.

Silky Oak
Grevillea robusta
PROTEACEAE

An evergreen tree with grey brown, fissured bark and an uneven, open crown. The spirally arranged leaves are deeply divided into long narrow lobes and are white and silky in appearance on the undersurface. Each leaf can be up to 30 cm long with 5–11 pairs of toothed or lobed segments. The small orange flowers are carried in short axillary spikes. This species grows well in the highlands but is not as robust in the lowlands.

Tutuk, Orange Tree Hibiscus
Hibiscus floccosus
MALVACEAE

Native to Malaysia. This is a deciduous tree with a rather narrow but cylindrical crown and smooth, pale grey bark. Leaves, young twigs and inflorescences are densely covered with harsh hair and scales. The heart shaped, leathery leaves have a stalk up to 7.5 cm long and a blade up to 20 cm wide. They are simple and spirally arranged. Flowers are in narrow, erect panicles. Each flower is with yellow or orange petals ten cm long. Fruits are oblong and about 3.8 cm wide. Propagated by seed. This species is useful in a mixed grouping as the deciduous character gives a change of aspect and young leaves are pink in colour when they develop.

Gelam Bukit
Leptospermum flavescens
MYRTACEAE

A small, evergreen tree up to 12 metres high, found in mountain areas. It has small, grey green leaves and an open crown with twisted branches covered with flaky fissured bark. The leaves are up to 3.8 cm long, lanceolate with a blunt apex and have a pleasant aromatic scent when crushed. The small, white flowers are axillary and are produced in large numbers near the ends of branches.

Petai Jawa
Leucaena leucocephala
LEGUMINOSAE

Native to tropical America but now found throughout the tropics. This is a small evergreen tree that can reach nine metres in height and has a light, feathery appearance. It is fast growing and can be pruned to keep the height under control. The bipinnate leaves are up to 38 cm long, with four to eight pairs of side stalks carrying 9–16 pairs of small leaflets. The leaflets are oblong with one side larger than the other and are 9–18 cm long and a quarter cm wide. The flowers are borne on round cream or white heads on long inflorescence stalk in the leaf axils. One or two flower heads develop in each leaf axil. Each flower head will produce several pods and these are 13–20 cm long, flat, with numerous seeds and become black at maturity. When the tree carried many ripen pods, it is somewhat untidy in appearance and so young pods should be removed as they form, if the tree is used as an ornamental. Propagation is very easy from seed. Will grow on most soils provided they are not too wet. Can be used in small gardens as it is easily controlled; or it can be used to make a light screen. Appropriate pruning is necessary when used for any operative purpose.

Mindi Kecil, Persian Lilac
Melia azederach
MELIACEAE

Cultivated in all warm climates and may have originated from North India. It is partly deciduous and young leaves begin to appear before all of the older ones have dropped. The spirally arranged leaves are bipinnate, sometimes tri-pinnate and will be up to 50 cm long. They have three to five pairs of side stalks each carrying three to five pairs of leaflets which are light green, narrow or elliptic and taper to the apex. The leaflet margin is strongly toothed. The flowers are carried in large axillary panicles and each flower is 1.3–1.9 cm wide with pink petals and pale purple, stamen tubes. Small indehiscent fruits are developed which are oval and become yellowish when ripe. Easily propagated by seeds.

Cempaka Putih
Michaelia alba
MAGNOLIACEAE

Not known wild but commonly cultivated in parks of South-East Asia. This species is evergreen, partly deciduous in the north, and can become a large tree of more than 21 metres in height with a conical or oblong crown when older. There appears to be some variation and in some specimens the crown is very dense whereas in others it is relatively thin. The bark is smooth and silvery grey. The leaves are light green and shiny of up to 25 cm long and 15 cm wide, elliptic in shape and tapering to the apex. The stalk is short, 1.3–3.8 cm long. The buds are covered with conical stipules that drop away and leave a ring-shaped scar on the young stems. Flowers are borne singly on the axils of the leaves and are about five cm long with white petals. They are very fragrant and are frequently sold in the market. Propagation by marcotting or cuttings. Good for general planting or mixed with other species.

Gemunggai, Horse-radish Tree
Moringa oleifera
MORINGACEAE

A widely cultivated tree native to North India. It is a small tree with a thin, open, irregular crown. It is a softwood and has tuberous roots. It is said to be evergreen but in Kuala Lumpur, it is deciduous The spirally arranged leaves are large pale green, and tripinnate or bipinnate with many small leaflets. Each leaf measures up to 50 cm in length and has a fern-like appearance. Flowers are produced on long, open panicles and are white in colour. Each panicle will carry several long, thick pods, green at first and becoming brown when ripe. They contain numerous seeds with three longitudinal wings. Easily grown from seeds or from both small and large cuttings. It can be used for ornamental purposes but it would be better to prune regularly so that only foliage is produced. When fruiting, it is rather untidy in appearance. Useful for variation in foliage grouping.

Petai
Parkia speciosa
LEGUMINOSAE

Native to Malaysia, this species usually is only thought of in association with the edible seeds, but not as an exceedingly handsome, large, evergreen tree that can reach 45 metres in height. The crown is variable in shape but is usually rather flat-topped or umbrella-shaped. In a well-grown tree the shape can be oblong. The long, stalked leaves are bipinnate with 10–20 pairs of side branches bearing very small, dark green leaflets. Each leaflet is oblong with a blunt open and an asymmetric base. The inflorescence resembles a drumstick as they have a long stalk carrying a large globular head of close-packed, cream-coloured flowers at the end. The flowers produce a great deal of nectar and have a strong, somewhat sickly smell. They are pollinated by bats and only the apical flowers develop fruits. Six to ten fruits develop in each inflorescence. The pods are green at first, becoming dark brown or black when they ripen. And when the tree is fruiting, the groups of young, light green pods give it distinctive appearance easily visible from a great distance. Pods are up to 50 cm long and six cm wide. They are usually collected when still green and are sold in the market. The trees are slow growing and on poor soil the crown will be thin. Propagation is from seeds which germinate quickly.

Medang Kelawar
Pygeum polystachum
ROSACEAE

A large deciduous tree of up to 27 metres in height with a round or conical, somewhat open crown. The leaves are large and broad, elliptic, light green and leathery in texture. They are 12−25 cm long and 6−13 cm wide with short stalks of up to 1.3 cm long and are alternately arranged. The yellow flowers are about 1.3 cm in diameter and are produced in short racemes at the time when the new young foliage develops.

Mempoyan, Silver Back
Rhodamnia trimerva
MYRTACEAE

A small evergreen tree of up to 15 metres high with opposite leaves which have three main veins. The crown is round to oval, grey brown, finely fissured bark. The leaves are 5−15 cm long and up to 7.5 cm broad, tapering to the apex which is often elongated. The under-surface of the leaf may be whitish or silvery because of a dense cover of short hairs. The very small flowers are produced in clusters on the leaf axils and are followed by small fruits of up to 1.3 cm wide which are black when ripe and eagerly sought after by birds.

Willow
Salix tetrasperma
SALICACEAE

A deciduous tree of up to 24 metres high with a cylindrical crown and branches which droop at the tips. The bark will develop deep furrows as the tree becomes older. Young twigs are reddish in colour. Leaves are lanceolate and tapered at both ends up to 15 cm long and four cm wide, dark green on the upper surface and slightly glaucous underneath. The small inconspicuous flowers are borne in catkins. The species is useful for planting along side streams or lakes. It is easily propagated by cuttings but can be subject to some damage from leaf-eating insects.

Kembang Semangkuk
Scaphium affine
STERCULIACEAE

A large tree that develops a short buttress and has spirally arranged, simple leaves. There is a very marked change in the leaf form between the sapling stage and the adult tree. In saplings the leaves are 30−60 cm long and broad with two to seven very large lobes and a stalk of up to 60 cm long. But in the adult tree the leaves are much smaller, up to 25 cm long and 15 cm broad, ovate, with an acute apex and a much shorter stalk of up to 15 cm long. The whole plant is covered with long, pale brown hairs. The inconspicuous flowers are carried in panicles and are followed by large, thin-walled, green pods containing one seed. The pods split along one side and the wall becomes thin and dry, acting as a wing for dispersal. The seeds give a great deal of mucilage when soaked in water.

Geti, Turi
Sesbania grandiflora
LEGUMINOSAE

A small, thin-crowned tree of up to about six metres high with a slender trunk and relatively few branches. It gives a very light shade. The pinnate leaves are long with many light green leaflets and the large pink or white flowers are carried in short racemes along the branches. It is a quick growing tree, but relatively shortlived and is easily propagated by seed which is freely produced. Young leaves and flowers are used as vegetables.

Sepalir
Sindora coriacea
LEGUMINOSAE

Large, slightly flat-topped trees with straight trunks and no buttresses. The leaves are pinnate with a few pairs of large, opposite leaflets and no terminal leaflet. The pods are oblong or disc-shaped, flattened and bear a number of short bristles over the whole surface. One or two seeds only are developed in each fruit.

Kelumpang
Sterculia foetida
STERULIACEAE

This species makes a large deciduous tree of up to 30 metres high and the trunk is without buttresses. It grows quickly when young and develops an open, somewhat conical crown with whorls of branches set 1.5 to two metres apart. The leaves are palmate and have five to nine leaflets held in a long stalk which is up to 20 cm in length. In very young tree the leaves may have more leaflets. The flowers are inconspicuous and are carried in short panicles at the ends of the twigs They give rise to large pods up to 10–15 cm long and broad, one flower produces four to five pods which become dark red when ripe and are arranged in a star-like pattern. When ripe, each pod splits along one margin and the large, oval, black seeds hang from the margin on very short stalks. They make attractive decoration but quickly dry and become brown. The

tree is often planted; but while young the crown can be irregular in shape because of the method of branching. Easily propagated from seeds which are produced regularly about once a year.

Pelawan
Tristania sumatrana
MYRTACEAE

The tree will reach 21 metres in height and normally grows along riverbanks. It is evergreen with a round, dense crown and flaking, orange brown bark. The shiny leaves are up to 18 cm long and five cm wide with an acute apex and at the base. The blade is tapered to a short stalk. The species flowers twice a year and the small flowers are produced in large clusters 7.5–15 cm long and are very conspicuous.

Bedara, Indian Jujube, Chinese Date
Zizyphus jujuba
RHAMACEAE

This is a small tree with an umbrella-shaped crown and may be from three to nine metres in height. The trunk is thick and stout with brown grey, deeply fissured bark and the crown becomes much more open in older trees. The main branches are spreading and the twigs are drooping with small thorns at the base of the leaf stalks. Flowers are tiny and inconspicuous, borne in clusters on the leaf axils. They give rise to oblong, round fruits up to three cm in diameter and are edible. The tree is more common in the north of the peninsula but can grow well farther south. The leaves are alternate, with toothed margins and three main veins. They are elliptic with broad, blunt apex and the undersurface is covered with dense, short, white brownish hairs. The species would probably be best used to give variation in foliage in groups of trees.